Development

SELECTED TOPICS

This book is in the
ADDISON-WESLEY SERIES IN LIFE SCIENCE

———————————

Consulting Editor
EDWARD HERBERT

LUCENA JAEGER BARTH

Barnard College

Development

SELECTED TOPICS

ADDISON-WESLEY PUBLISHING COMPANY, INC.

READING, MASSACHUSETTS · PALO ALTO · LONDON

Preface

Several years ago the writer was invited to teach an undergraduate college course whose prospectus stated that "An historical survey will be made of discoveries in a specific field of biology, and these will be analyzed as examples of the manner in which scientific knowledge is accumulated." Accepting this challenging invitation, the writer looked about for an appropriate text suitable for the subject and for second-year college students. None was available that broached the subject from precisely the point of view required: a detailed study of *experiments* basic to the evolution of concepts in a specific area of biology.

We were forced therefore into the stimulating task of organizing lectures and laboratories upon the basis of a synthesis of materials from the original literature, advanced textbooks, proceedings of meetings and symposia, and our own experience with active research over a period of years. Conceivably an entire family of courses could be built up with the general objectives noted above.

Students have responded with enthusiasm to this idea of learning the facts of a given field in the context of past, contemporary, and possible future ideas and experiments. The emphasis has had to be upon a critical analysis of a few major lines of investigation—since time and (in a book) space are limited. On the basis of our experience at Barnard College, it may be said that by the end of this course, undergraduates have a better comprehension of why past experiments have not yet solved some of the basic problems. They read the original literature in more critical frame of mind, write a term paper on a topic of active contemporary research, and look forward with excitement to future advances.

We believe that this kind of organization of subject matter could provide profitable collateral reading for undergraduate courses in general biology, embryology, genetics, and for undergraduate seminars, even where a concepts course is not included in the curriculum.

In the present book we have undertaken to present one example of this kind of approach to one area of biology: some aspects of embryonic development. The particular subjects chosen for analysis concern nucleo-cytoplasmic interactions. The *experimental* approach to this subject has a history in time of little more than seventy-five years. Its future promises exciting advances, as a result of progress in cell biology in general and molecular genetics in particular.

Above all, this book is directed toward our current undergraduates, among whom are our embryologists of the future. As J. Lederberg has said, eventually embryology will have to be studied in embryos.

We have been especially fortunate in having the manuscript read critically by Doctors Martha Barnes Baylor and Lester G. Barth, both of whom have been generous in time and encouragement. For any ambiguities that may remain the writer takes full responsibility.

Woods Hole, Massachusetts   L. J. B.
August 1963

Contents

With this book
the author pays tribute to Barnard College
on the occasion of its Seventy-Fifth Anniversary

1

A Challenge

"Our intellectual ancestors would perhaps be pleased that we have come so far in clarifying their riddles. But they would be amused, too, that we still tread a path they knew well, and still look forward with excitement to new answers to old questions. . . . this uncertainty, this sense of future discovery, this opportunity to glimpse previously undetected clues in the ever-changing panorama of development—all make the embryo an especially seducing challenge to all who have grappled with it."

M. V. Edds, Jr.

This book is written in a deliberately chronological style. It represents an attempt to trace, through the past seventy years, the evolution of some of the concepts which have arisen from the study of development, and to present a summary of some contemporary viewpoints which are providing launching sites for future investigations of developmental phenomena.

What value obtains to such an historical approach? Why not begin with the present status of this area of biological investigation and look only to the future? Are we simply to write an account of past "errors," of what often now appear to have been naive viewpoints as compared with the present level of relative sophistication in terms of "molecular biology"? We firmly believe that, first of all, such a chronological approach possesses an intellectual fascination with respect to the manner in which scientific knowledge is accumulated by individual investigators and by any one generation of investigators. More than this, however, the gradualness, humility, and passion (to borrow Pavlov's terms) that have gone into the work of many of the investigators in this area may serve as encouragement to those of us who are contemporary investigators of the problems of development, problems so long ago comprehended but not yet solved.

Largely because of the recent breakthrough in "cracking" the genetic code we feel closer than we can imagine any previous generation to have been to solving many of the problems of cellular differentiation and development. It is to be hoped that this aspect of nucleocytoplasmic interactions in control of specific protein syntheses as discussed in the last chapter will indeed soon be comprehended in embryonic systems.

We are not unique, however, in this anticipation of imminent discovery. Indeed this excitement and hope are (and surely must always have been) what keeps an investigator going through his routine, day to day work. But if we examine the past history of our field, we learn that previous generations of biologists also have believed that the concepts most popular at their time were about to solve all the problems.

Thus it is with a poignant feeling that one reads a footnote written in 1934 on page 12 of Huxley and De Beer's classic and otherwise undated *The Elements of Experimental Embryology*. "Already it is known that the organising action is due to a substance which is almost certainly lipoidal and probably a sterol. . . ." Anyone acquainted with the current status of developmental biology three decades later will readily attest to the fact that the chemical nature of the organizer still is obscure. The whole character of inductive phenomena remains enigmatic despite attacks upon the problem from many different vantage points.

We hope by this book to stimulate enthusiasm in young readers for careers devoted to attacking the problems of development. We may reassure them that there will be many problems still to be solved when they have received their basic training for research. "Wait for me; don't solve all the problems before I get there," a former student confessed to have said when first introduced to the study of embryology. We won't! We can't! And perhaps the following account of some aspects of the study of development will help to explain why not—yet.

This book will be concerned with some aspects of the concept of biological continuity. A comprehensive treatment of this concept cannot be achieved in so brief a book. A comprehensive work would need to include information drawn from studies of heredity and evolution. We can touch only briefly and in a peripheral manner upon these areas of information, and will confine ourselves for the most part to the study of what has come to be known as "developmental" biology. If we succeed in our objectives, however, it should become apparent that there is no distinct boundary line between developmental biology and other areas of biology, but rather a distinct interdependence.

We will analyze, criticize, and invite the reader's critical appraisal of a number of *experiments,* attempting to present their conceptual background and details of execution insofar as space permits. Thus, further delimitation will be necessary in choice of illustrative experiments and organisms. The writer will use primarily studies on amphibian development. The amphibian egg was one of the first objects to be studied by experimental methods, and still constitutes a widely used material for studies on the many aspects of differentiation and development.

This choice, however, reflects no prejudice on the part of the writer that the amphibian egg is the ideal material for study. In fact, the egg is a rather poor choice of material for studies on the initial phases of differentiation, which might with at least equal profit be carried out with, say, the egg of *Fucus* (a marine brown alga), dissociated cells of a sponge, or amoeboid stages of a slime mold. Indeed we share the conviction expressed by Wilhelm Roux, a pioneer in developmental biology, who in 1895 tells us that this field "utilizes for its own purposes all methods which may be productive of causal understanding and all biological disciplines . . ." and suggests that "it embrace as its field of investigation all living things, from the lowest Protista to the highest animal and vegetable organisms [54]."*

Today, some sixty-five years later, a glance at the contents of one of the journals devoted to problems of development reveals just such a broad representation of organisms and methods. A single-celled green alga, a ciliated protozoan, coelenterates, flatworms, arthropods—indeed perhaps no phylum has been neglected by one or another investigator of problems of development. For these problems go far beyond the single example presented by development of an embryo.

The methods employed are as varied as the materials and specific problems. Here an investigator is injecting embryonic proteins into a rabbit to obtain antisera; another has made electron microscope photographs through the regenerating stump of a salamander's limb; a third investigator, using polarized light, has photographed the asters and spindle of the mitotic apparatus in a *living* egg. Still another has accomplished the delicate task of removing a nucleus from one kind of cell and injecting it into a second cell. In another laboratory, embryonic tissues have been dissociated into their component cells and their subsequent reorganization followed. Another paper describes the injection of a radioisotope into an embryo and its later distribution during development. And that classical material of experimental embryology, the amphibian egg, continues to be subjected to every variety of technique that biochemistry and physiology have to offer. The frog egg and embryo have been homogenized, centrifuged, assayed for enzymes. The proteins of the embryo have been subjected to electrophoresis; its respiration as a whole and that of its various regions have been measured.

What are the basic problems common to all these different modes of attack? What contemporary concepts are held concerning these problems? What kinds of experiments have formed the basis for the evolution of these concepts over the past sixty odd years? And, above all, what experiments may be done next? These are questions which we shall discuss in the following chapters.

---

* Numbers in brackets are keyed to the References at the rear of the book.

2

Problems of Continuity and Diversity in Living Systems

The specific problems of development all arise in the context of a comprehensive biological concept, the continuity of life. The bridge between successive generations is quite obvious in most members of both animal and plant kingdoms. Part of an organism separates off from the parent and either unites with a cell of opposite "mating type" as in the many varieties of sexual reproduction; or the parent organism may simply split into two or more parts and by growth alone reattain the parental size, as in fission, budding, and fragmentation. In any event, continuity between successive generations is clearly manifest.

A little reflection, however, reveals that an important aspect of biological continuity must be reconciled with this simple picture of the physical bridge between generations. Equally characteristic of life is change. There are short-term, reversible physiological alterations such as muscle contraction and nerve conduction. The relatively longer term changes represented in development and evolution must be placed in context with the concept of continuity.

Offspring are similar but not always identical with the parent. Evolutionary change indeed is considered by most biologists to depend in part upon such differences between parents and offspring—differences that have their bases in chromosomal and gene mutations as well as in the differences that arise when genes and chromosomes are shuffled in the processes of sexual reproduction. These changes, together with differential reproduction within populations, are among the major "forces of evolution" [57].

Our concept of continuity must therefore include provision for concomitant change. As Simpson points out, "Man is . . . akin nearly or remotely to all of life and indeed to all that is material." For if one begins to trace his biological "genealogy" backward in time, he must admit kinship with the first self-replicating molecules that arose on this planet. Indeed to some enquiring minds even this is not the stopping point, or better, the beginning. For the origin of self-replicating molecules, organic compounds had previously to have arisen; for organic molecules to have been available, appropriate atomic configurations were prerequisite, and so on.

This molecular interpretation of continuity is not, of course, to be taken in the naive sense of actual passing on from one generation to another and from one evolutionary period to another of actual physical molecules from a stockpile built up at the "beginning" of life on earth. Such a concept of molecular preformation is untenable—in absolute disagreement with what we know about the dynamic state of the components of living matter. Radioisotopes (of amino acids, fatty acids, organic bases, and so on) injected into an adult organism or embryo exchange with their specific unlabeled counterparts, until quite rapidly the injected isotope molecules are built into the tissues or parts of cells of the injected organism.

Biological continuity must be based upon transmission not of a limited number of molecules formed in pre-biological times, but rather upon transmission of a specific molecular pattern. The pattern must have elements of both constancy and of capacity for change, in order to be consistent with the continuity of life and with the origin of changes of potential significance for evolution. The molecular basis for such a pattern therefore demands peculiar, special properties. The molecules involved must be able to form replicas of themselves, replicas subject to modification, and in addition enter into the synthesis of other kinds of molecules lacking the property of self-replication.

Replication of structural patterns is common to all cells that are undergoing mitosis. In a developing system, however, an additional feature is added: replication of likeness, together with the origin of new patterns of enzymes, of cytoplasmic ultramicrostructural components, of histological characteristics, as well as the grosser form changes that represent the more obvious progressive phases of developmental processes. It is with this type of change with time that we shall be concerned in the following chapters.

In sexual reproduction, germ cells, which represent the only physical link between successive generations, arise from the zygote. But so also do all the other so-called somatic cells which perish with death of the organism and hence cannot be directly involved in our concept of continuity. Within each individual ontogeny a variety of cell types arise, and become organized into tissues, organs, and organ systems. By what means during the developmental process is provision made for retention of the full complement of hereditary determinants to be passed on to the next generation? Or are the visible structural and functional characteristics of differentiated cells of the late embryo and adult misleading? Could some seemingly differentiated cells under favorable conditions reverse their differentiation processes and form one or more different kinds of cells?

In some plants, this latter potentiality is manifest. An entire *Begonia* plant with its vascular tissues, leaves, stems, etc., can develop from a bud composed purely of adult epidermal cells [20, p. 18]. Among animals, regeneration phenomena in coelenterates, platyhelminths, nemertians, and lower vertebrates (to mention only a few examples) similarly broach the question of whether differentiation is an irreversible event. Alternative possibilities include: (1) some "totipotent" cells are reserved during differentiation to serve as primitive germ cells or to be available for muster when regeneration is stimulated; (2) dedifferentiation of cells to a totipotent state takes place followed by redifferentiation; or (3) no true dedifferentiation occurs, but rather a reshuffling and sorting out again of differentiated cells which retain their specific properties throughout the regeneration cycle.

Stated in broadest terms then, the basic problems of development as we see them still today are of two types: (1) the origin of differences within one generation, and (2) continuity between generations. In the first category arise such questions as the manner in which genes and cytoplasm interact during the sequential changes characteristic of development; the extent and circumstances under which such changes may be reversible; the nature of interactions between cells during development. Into the second category falls the puzzle of whether germ cells "retain or regain" the full hereditary complement and whether in this respect they are truly different from somatic cells.

3

Historical Formulation
of Working Hypotheses

It is perhaps fitting that in a treatise on continuity any starting point must be arbitrary and that the end will represent but the contemporary baseline for further elaboration of information in the field. Faced with the necessity of interrupting this continuum, let us choose the year 1882. In this year, Wilhelm Roux heated a needle in a flame and thrust its hot point into one of the first two blastomeres of a frog egg that had just completed first cleavage. The results and extensions of this experiment will be discussed in Chapter 5.

Any meaningful experiment has conceptual antecedents and bears the stamp of the experimental work and thinking of many individuals. During the years immediately following the epic publications of Darwin and Wallace, all of biological thought was permeated by the concept of evolution. In the case of development of a vertebrate embryo, for example, emphasis was laid upon the external resemblances of the various successive phases of its development to the adult forms of lower vertebrates. Thus the mammalian embryo progresses through "stages" that bear a crude resemblance to adult fish and amphibians. The existence of these resemblances, by no means universal and certainly only rough approximations of earlier phyla, was dignified by the "law" that "ontogeny recapitulates phylogeny." As Spemann [60] later wrote: "It had been forgotten by many that the changes of form constituting the outer aspect of development must have, besides their hypothetical derivation from adult states of times long ago, their immediate physical causes, the investigation of which might also be a worthy scientific task and, perhaps, the more urgent one."

It was during this period of speculation and theory, the last decades of the nineteenth century, that the writings of August Weismann among others began to pose more specific problems of development, later to be elaborated and attacked by experimentalists dissatisfied with vague analogies between evolution and development. Some of Weismann's theoretical constructs later were rejected on the basis of experimental evidence. The impact of his writings came largely from his clear, concise formulation of the problems implicit in continuity between successive generations of organisms, and diversification within a particular developmental process [29].

Weismann's theoretical contructs fall into two categories: (1) continuity of the germ plasm, and (2) unequal distribution of hereditary determinants during development. Continuity of the germ plasm was a concept devised by Weismann to answer the question: How is it that "a single cell of the body [germ cell] can contain within itself all the hereditary tendencies of the whole organism . . . ?" Weismann suggested three theoretical possibilities.

1. Darwin's theory of pangenesis was rejected by Weismann. This theory assumed that all cells of the organism dispatch small particles to the germ cells. The latter then would represent an extract of the whole body. This theory, quite impossible to test experimentally in Weismann's time, is even less tenable today in terms of modern genetics. True enough it has recently been shown that some proteins from the maternal blood stream are transferred through the protective follicle cells that surround the ovarian egg into the egg itself. There is nothing to indicate, however, the kind of stockpiling in the egg of hereditary particles endowed with genetic continuity from the blood stream suggested by Darwin.

2. A second possibility envisioned by Weismann was that the substance of the germ cell (egg) is capable of undergoing a series of changes, which after resulting in formation of the new individual "lead back again to identical germ cells."

3. The hypothesis favored by Weismann was that germ cells are not derived at all from the body of the individual but directly from the parent germ cell, or rather from a substance within the parent germ cell which Weismann called the "germ plasm." He assigned to the germ plasm the property of having a specific molecular constitution, of sufficient complexity to endow it with power to develop into a complex organism. During each ontogeny, the germ plasm contained in the parent egg cell is not used up in construction of the body of the offspring but is "reserved unchanged" for formation of the germ cells of the following generation. The germ plasm, Weismann suggested, increases in quantity by "assimilation" but remains qualitatively the same.

Weismann's criterion of a molecular specificity required for germ plasm is, we know today, met by some properties of the nucleic acids. But the actual physical "setting aside" of such molecules during the differentiation process is highly dubious, and certainly unlikely in the sense in which Weismann indicated.

To summarize, the concept of continuity of germ plasm assumes that certain molecules of the egg remain unchanged as the embryo develops.

When the ovary forms, it is populated by egg cells containing these molecules, which therefore become incorporated into the eggs that are the physical basis for the next generation. Recall that this theory was formulated years before the rediscovery of Mendel's experiments. Furthermore, when Weismann was writing, even the relative importance of the nucleus in the life of the cell was largely a matter for speculation. We shall discuss this concept at some length below, but first let us outline the second aspect of Weismann's hypothesis—unequal distribution of hereditary determinants during development.

This concept derived from Weismann's conviction that the origin of differences between cells had to depend upon differences in their "nucleoplasm." "The simplest hypothesis," he says, "would be to suppose that, at each division of the nucleus, its specific substance divides into two halves of unequal quality, so that the cell-bodies would also be transformed. . . ." Thus was proposed an ordered process of parcelling out of nuclear determinants (genes) among the cells derived by cleavage from the zygote. This qualitative nuclear division of hypothetical hereditary units would demand some controlling principle so that an orderly organism of definite character results. A kind of "super-marshal" would be needed to see that each determinant would get into its proper cell, and would supply the cell with accessory determinants to provide for possible regeneration! Needless to say, this theory in its original form did not survive. But as we shall see in a later chapter, it formed part of the background for the first *experiments* with *living* embryos. Furthermore, during the past decade, this theory in more subtle form has been revived in connection with recent studies of nuclear differentiation to be discussed later.

In the next chapter we will be concerned with the contributions of more modern experimental methods to Weismann's first postulate, continuity of the germ plasm.

4

Tracking the Germ Cells

Today, more than sixty years since Weismann's writings, what can be said about the question of continuity of the germ plasm between generations? Why is this problem so refractory toward solution? It will occur to you that conclusive proof for continuity would depend upon marking the germ plasm in some irreversible manner such that this material, if it exists, can be traced unequivocally from egg through embryo to adult ovary to functional egg of the next generation. How can this be achieved? Can we find a nontoxic stain for germ plasm so specific that this material alone and no other type of molecule will take up and hold onto the stain? Is there any way of keeping track of a group of molecules through a series of generations? And even if there is, what evidence can be presented that these molecules are responsible for qualities that distinguish germ cells from all other cells of the body?

The difficulties that have beset the problem of tracking primordial germ cells from the time they are first claimed to be recognizable in the early embryo to the time when these cells appear in the newly formed gonad of the later embryo are numerous. These difficulties provide a classical example of the fact that not only do various investigators of the same problem differ in their theories—but that the validity of an observation, a "fact," may be open to question depending upon the method used to establish that "fact."

MORPHOLOGICAL EVIDENCE IN VERTEBRATE EMBRYOS

Restricting ourselves to vertebrate embryos, we find in the literature even as far back as the 1880's claims that primordial germ cells arise in outlying endodermal or mesodermal regions and subsequently migrate into the developing gonads. The origin of the somatic cells of the gonads in vertebrate embryos is clearly agreed upon as mesodermal [2]. The germinal (or genital) ridges which differentiate into the paired gonads are longitudinal strips of thickened mesoderm lying alongside the dorsal mesentery and protruding into the coelomic cavity (Fig. 1). The somatic cells contained in the germinal ridges form the various supporting and protecting cells of the mature gonad.

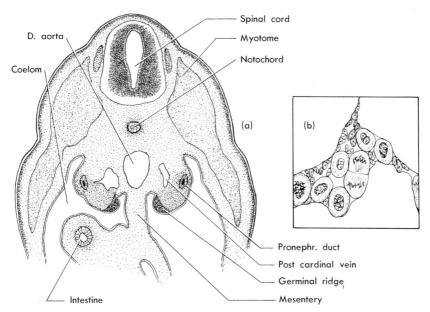

FIGURE 1. Origin of the gonads. (a) Cross section through a mouse embryo to show the position of the germinal ridges which differentiate into the paired gonads. (b) Section through rudimentary gonad of a frog showing contrast between larger presumed primordial germ cells and smaller somatic cells. (From Balinsky, 1960, after A. Brachet, 1935.)

We must first question the criteria used for purported identification of primordial germ cells. In the rudimentary gonad, sectioned and stained, two morphologically distinct cell types are seen: small somatic cells, and large cells tentatively identified as primordial germ cells. The latter are not only relatively large, round cells, but also are characterized by clear, vesicular nuclei. In the amphibian embryo they are rich in yolk platelets, as compared with other cells.

When progressively earlier embryos are sectioned and searched for cells possessing these morphological peculiarities, such cells are observed in areas outside the rudimentary gonad. It has been surmised, therefore, on the basis of histological sections, that primordial germ cells migrate from outlying points of origin into the rudimentary gonad of vertebrate embryos. More specifically it has been stated that in the amphibian embryo, for example, at advanced tailbud stages, the primordial germ cells appear in the endoderm at the highest mid-dorsal ridge of the endoderm cell mass underlying the aorta. Later they are pinched off as the lateral plate mesoderm closes in from both sides. Later still the ridge in which they lie is displaced by formation of new blood vessels, and the germ cells move laterally into the already formed primitive, indifferent gonads [2, 70].

Pushing the history of these so-called primordial germ cells still further back, in certain amphibia they had been tentatively identified some thirty years ago as early as late cleavage stages [11]. More recent studies [9] proved that in the frogs *Rana temporaria* and *R. pipiens* shortly after the egg is fertilized a certain dye (Azure A) is taken up by cytoplasm located near the vegetal pole. This dye stains nucleic acids. Even parthenogenetically activated eggs form this special cytoplasm, so that the sperm does not contribute directly to its genesis, but perhaps indirectly, as part of the cortical reaction that follows upon activation of the egg. During cleavage this cytoplasm becomes incorporated into cells that move upward and lie in, or within a few cell layers below, the blastocoele floor.

During gastrulation these cells (numbering less than two dozen) move from the upper regions of the endoderm into deeper lying regions of the endoderm, where they are seen in the young neurula. By hatching, these tentatively identifiable primordial germ cells have migrated from the deep endoderm position upward and laterally around the archenteron until they come to temporary rest in the mid-dorsal crest of endoderm. Henceforth their movements into the primitive gonads follow the pattern outlined in the paragraph above. It should be mentioned that by gastrulation the specific staining properties of these cells become increasingly diminished, presumably as a result of decreased ribonucleic acid content.

EXPERIMENTAL EVIDENCE

In chick and mammalian embryos, a similar migratory history has been described on the basis of histological sections of embryos at successive stages of development. When we come to examine actual experimental evidence, however, the picture becomes more ambiguous. While it is not possible to interfere experimentally with events in mammalian (including human) embryos, the lower vertebrates such as amphibia and chicks are available for an experimental approach to our question.

There is reasonable agreement among various workers that primordial germ cells arise in the chick embryo in the endodermal layer at the anterior border of the extraembryonic portion of the blastoderm, a region called the germinal crescent. Experimental evidence for identification of these cells as primordial germ cells depends upon absence of germ cells in the gonad following earlier extirpation or irradiation of the germinal crescent (references in 2). Further experiments have been made to discover the manner in which primordial germ cells make their long journey from an area completely outside the embryo proper to their destination in the primitive gonads [56]. Two alternatives have been suggested:

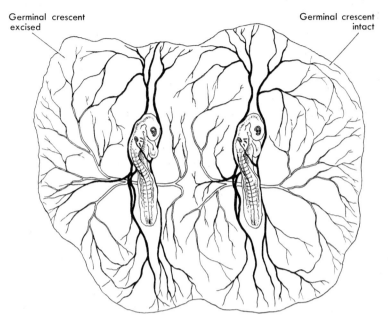

Germinal crescent
excised

Germinal crescent
intact

FIGURE 2. Parabiotic twins in the chick embryo. Two embryos are united by their extraembryonic areas at a stage before migration of primary germ cells has begun. Their vascular systems remain independent; only their nonvascular tissues unite. The germinal crescent had been removed from the embryo on the left only. When sectioned later the embryo on the left was sterile. The embryo on the right possessed primordial germ cells in its gonads. (After Simon, 1957.)

amoeboid motion through the tissues, or passage through the blood stream of the young blastoderm.

When a chick embryo is still at the ten-somite stage (about 30 hours of incubation), the primordial germ cells are grouped at the anterior border of the extraembryonic area in the germinal crescent. After four days of development, they are seen in the young gonads.

Parabiotic twins were made, using two young embryos at the ten-somite stage before migration of the germ cells had begun. The germinal crescent had been cut away from one of these embryos before uniting them through their extraembryonic areas and culturing them *in vitro*. Although most of the tissues of the twin blastoderms fused together, their vascular systems remained separate; no connections were formed between the blood vessels of the parabionts. Four days later, when sectioned, the gonads of the normal member of the pair contained primordial germ cells, while the embryo from which the germinal crescent had been removed was completely sterile, lacking any germ cells whatsoever (Fig. 2).

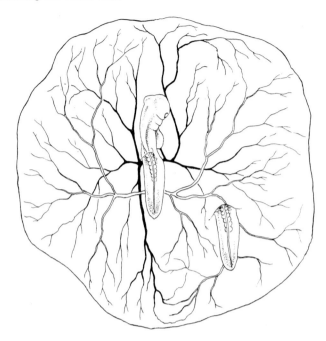

FIGURE 3. Graft of a posterior region of a chick embryo into the extraembryonic region of another embryo. Both donor and host were at a stage of less than 10 somites; therefore neither possessed primordial germ cells in the presumptive gonad regions at the time of operation. Later the supplementary gonad becomes populated with primordial germ cells as a result of migration of these cells from the germinal crescent through the blood stream into both host and donor gonads. (After Simon, 1957.)

From this experiment alone it might be argued that the distance was too great for the germ cells to migrate by amoeboid motion from the intact germinal crescent into the operated parabiont gonad during the time elapsed. Another kind of experiment, however, serves to discount this objection and to implicate the blood vascular system directly as the channel for transport of the germ cells. Here, as shown in Fig. 3, a supplementary posterior part of an embryo including the future gonad was grafted into the extraembryonic area of another intact embryo at somewhat earlier than the ten-somite stage, and the whole operated blastoderm was cultivated *in vitro*. In this instance, the host vascular system invaded the graft, and both host and graft continued to differentiate normally, forming somites, limb buds, and so on. When this interesting combination was sectioned and observed histologically, the supplementary graft contained numerous germ cells, as did also, of course, the host gonad.

These experiments speak forcibly against the hypothesis that in the bird embryo, germ cells reach their destination by amoeboid movement through the layers of embryonic tissues. The results favor the hypothesis that germ cells are carried in the blood stream from their site of origin to the rudimentary gonad. Why they selectively take up residence only in the gonads is another problem. It has been observed that some germ cells do go astray and, failing to reach the gonad, degenerate. Conversely, if the primordial germ cells are prevented from reaching the germinal ridge, the latter fails to differentiate into a gonad [2]. Such a developmentally significant mutual dependence of two parts of an embryo is referred to as embryonic induction, a phenomenon we shall have occasion to mention again.

A similar relationship exists in the mammal, where also the primitive germ cells appear first in outlying endodermal regions from which they migrate (probably by amoeboid movement) into the young gonad, which is forming from intermediate mesoderm [70].

In the amphibian embryo, however, the experimental results have been rather conflicting. On the one hand, transplantation experiments between embryos of two species of newts whose cells differ in pigmentation have suggested that the primary germ cells originate in the mesoderm [51]. At the neurula stage, entire endodermal masses were interchanged between two embryos of the pigmented and unpigmented species respectively (Fig. 4). The transplanted endodermal masses were introduced into the empty ectodermal-mesodermal "shells" of the opposite pigment type. Complete removal of all endoderm cells from the mesectodermal shell or envelope was claimed to have been accomplished. When primordial germ cells later could be recognized, their type corresponded not to that of the transplanted endoderm, but to the pigment character of the ecto-mesodermal "shell." The species differences in pigmentation were not all-or-none. Even the "nonpigmented" cells contained a few (2 to 17) pigment granules, while the "pigmented" cells ranged in granule content from very few to very many in a graded series. Nonetheless, these experiments provided evidence for a mesodermal source of primordial germ cells.

Other experiments have been made, however, which suggest an endodermal origin for the amphibian primitive germ cells. When the hypothetical presumptive germ cell area of the endoderm is removed by surgery [2], or is subjected to ultraviolet irradiation [2], gonads later form in the experimental animals, but the quantity of germ cells is much reduced, or sometimes there are no germ cells present at all. It might be hypothesized that removal or damage to this specific area of the endoderm destroys the inductive properties of the endoderm necessary to stimulate differentiation of the gonad (and possibly formation of primi-

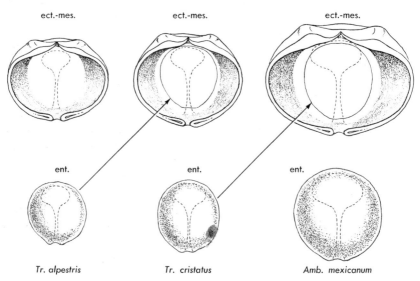

FIGURE 4. Transplantation of endodermal masses among three species of amphibians. Primordial germ cells that later develop possess the pigmentation characteristic of the ectomesodermal envelope and not that of the transplanted endoderm. The *Triton cristatus* neurula is too large for its unpigmented endodermal mass to be inserted into an envelope of ectomesoderm of *Triton alpestris*. Hence the larger neurula of pigmented *Ambystoma mexicanum* serves as host in the right-hand operation. (After Nieuwkoop, 1946.)

tive germ cells from the mesoderm). Such an hypothesis would partially reconcile the interspecific endodermal transplantation studies mentioned above. A further deduction then would be that the endodermal inductive factors are quite general, i.e., not species specific.

In this connection it was claimed many years ago [52] that the ovaries in mammals can regenerate after being removed by operation. These regenerated ovaries were said to contain oocytes, which of course would have to have come from the somatic (epithelial) tissues adjacent to the ovary, the peritoneal epithelium. Here the endoderm could have played no role, either as source or inductor of germ cells.

THE NUCLEOLAR MARKER AS A TOOL

Still another question has troubled the thoughtful student of the continuity dilemma. Regardless of whether characteristic cells can be tracked from outlying regions into the ovary, or whether characteristic "germ cell-like" cells appear to arise from somatic tissues of the ovary—the basic problem is to prove whether or not these cells give rise to the

sex cells for the following generation. The special cytological characteristics of the so-called primordial germ cells become obliterated after
early stages of development, and it becomes increasingly difficult to
distinguish them from somatic cells of the gonad. The problem is further
complicated by the large number of mitotic divisions that intervene
between primordial germ cells and mature ovum, and by the fact that a
large number of the resulting cells undergo degeneration along the way.
For example, in the human embryo it has been estimated [70] that at
four weeks, the developing gonad contains about one hundred primordial
germ cells. At twenty weeks, an estimated 5,000,000 are present, while
the mature young female gonad contains only about four hundred.
Clearly the chain of continuity is a tenuous one here.

Let us look at one ingenious method that has recently been applied to
the problem. The experiments require much time because one must
breed offspring from crosses between test animals and wildtype individuals of the South African clawed toad, *Xenopus laevis*, and eight
months are required for each generation. The experiments were beautifully designed, and the results have provided the first conclusive proof
in favor of a very precocious origin if not actual continuity of the germ
line in vertebrates.

A few years ago a group of workers at Oxford University [59, 26] were
studying methods of producing ploidy (extra chromosome sets) in *Xenopus*. To diagnose their results they made "squashes" of bits of the tail
tips of the experimental animals by means of which the chromosomes
were spread out sufficiently to be counted. They were also depending
upon the convenient fact that each haploid set of chromosomes includes
one particular chromosome which possesses a nucleolar organizing region
(NOR). The nucleolus is a specialized nongenic structure thought to be
implicated in some not as yet clearly defined manner with the synthesis
of nuclear proteins. As a diagnostic feature for estimating ploidy, a
normal wildtype diploid cell would contain two nucleoli, one for each
haploid set of chromosomes. Tetraploid cells experimentally produced
should contain four haploid sets and four nucleoli.

An alert worker in the laboratory observed that in one experiment
only one nucleolus (1N) per diploid set (2n) of chromosomes was present
in a *Xenopus* tadpole. This odd individual was raised to maturity and
proved to be a female. She was mated with a number of different males
and her progeny were analyzed for number of nucleoli per diploid set of
chromosomes. Her one-nucleolar condition proved to be a simple Mendelian character, lack of a nucleolar organizing region on the appropriate
chromosome of one haploid set. She was heterozygous for the nuclear
marker. The eggs she produced thus were of two classes, one lacking the
NOR, the other possessing it. Crossed with a wildtype male, approxi-

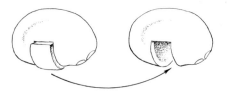

FIGURE 5. Scheme of germ-cell transfer operation in neurulae of *Xenopus laevis*. (After Blackler and Fischberg, 1961.)

mately half her offspring were normal for two nucleoli (2N), the other half deficient 1N in nucleolar content.

Here then was a "built-in" marker for following the fate of germ cells from one generation to the next. Unlike a dye that will be diluted, or an isotope that may be lost from dying cells into the medium, the nucleolar marker is part of the cell's own structure. The Oxford group (now at Geneva) proceeded to design experiments utilizing this marker as a means of following the germ line. As we have already mentioned, one member of this group (Blackler) previously had localized what he believed to be the presumptive germ cell cytoplasm of the egg as the Azure A-stainable cytoplasm near the vegetal pole of the newly fertilized egg. At the neurula stage, this cytoplasm could be found in cells located in the mid-ventral yolk-endoderm region. This neat localization of presumptive germ cell materials suggested the classical technique of transplantation. It was proposed to transplant this presumptive germ cell region at the neurula stage from a 1N mutant embryo into the corresponding endodermal region of a normal 2N neurula (Fig. 5). Assuming normal development and the usual morphogenetic movements and cell migrations, one would then expect an adult whose somatic cells are 2N in character and whose germ cells are 1N. Thus if some of the donor cells actually migrate into the host gonad and form functional germ cells, this recipient would behave as a 1N parent. When crossed with a wildtype known to be 2N, we might expect from classical Mendelian ratios to obtain approximately 50% 1N offspring among the progeny.

GAMETES AND OFFSPRING FROM A CROSS
BETWEEN 2N × 1N INDIVIDUALS

	1N	1N
1N	2N	2N
0N	1N	1N

The recently published results [10] of these experiments bear out the above expectation: both 2N and 1N offspring appeared among the progeny of the transplantation animal crossed with a 2N mate. The ratio approximated 50 1N to 50 2N per 100 embryos. Thus as these investigators conclude, ". . . primordial germ cells actually exist in neurula stages . . . and . . . they are directly ancestral to at least some of the definitive eggs and sperm."

GERM CELL VERSUS SOMATIC CELL DETERMINATION: A QUERY

These experiments are consistent with Weismann's hypothesis that the germ plasm is set apart very early in the development of vertebrate embryos. Yet why should only one type of cellular differentiation be so carefully secluded? We have noted that although the germ plasm appears just after fertilization or activation, the definitive gonocytes appear just before the beginning of gastrulation. Later on, when gastrulation has been completed, other groups of cells similarly have been set upon their pathways of differentiation—toward nerve, muscle, skin, and so on. These latter regions of the egg at the early gastrula stage still were capable of many kinds of differentiation. Is it not possible that determination of which cells shall form gonocytes differs in time, being more precocious, but not in principle, from any other kind of cell that arises during development?

Endoderm in general is known to become determined before other types of cells (although it actually differentiates later than nerve and muscle). Thus by late gastrula in some amphibians even the subregions of the gut (liver, pancreas, stomach, etc.) have become fixed as to their future differentiation [38].

A further question now comes to mind. The germ cells localized by Azure A staining retain their yolk and ribonucleic acid (RNA) longer than surrounding endoderm cells. Does this peculiarity result from the position in which these cells find themselves in relation to the egg as a whole? Or are the cytoplasmic peculiarities a result of differences in germ cell nuclei as distinguished from somatic cell nuclei of, say, presumptive nerve, muscle, or epidermal cells? We shall have occasion to return to this intriguing question later on.

One might speculate as to what hints could be obtained as to the mechanism of somatic versus germ cell determination from a study of one of the first evolutionary occurrences of such a distinction among the colonial protozoa. Among the Family *Volvocidae*, whose members resemble plants rather than animals, a series of forms occur which represent not only increasing numbers of individuals comprising a colony but also increasing specialization between somatic and germ cells. *Eudorina illinoisensis* is composed of a group of thirty-two flagellate cells, of which twenty-eight are larger and can form gametes (cells of opposite mating types, whose union leads to formation of a zygote from which new colonies arise). The other four cells are smaller, incapable of sexual reproduction, and cannot form gametes. These colonial protozoa present the problem of the fundamental control of somatic versus germ cell determination in such challenging simplicity that one wonders why contemporary investigators do not turn to them as materials for fresh inroads into the problem. Are the nuclei of incipient somatic cells qualitatively identical with those of germ cells? Could a simple environmental factor be applied in gradient fashion so as to determine which cells of the colony become restricted to the somatic type of differentiation?

In *Eudorina illinoisensis*, for example, the presumptive somatic cells are localized during development of a colony at the "lips" of a colony of cells whose overall structure resembles that of an early gastrula such as is seen in *Amphioxus*. In both instances, quite simple factors might be invoked to explain the origin of differences between cells at the lips of the invaginated ball of cells and those cells more deeply situated within. The fact that we cannot as yet specify the precise biochemical reactions needed to link simple factors such as gradients in pH, availability of oxygen, excretion of carbon dioxide, and so on, to specific end results in cellular differentiation should present more challenge than discouragement.

In some of the invertebrates (the mollusc *Sphaerium striatinum;* the roundworm, *Ascaris megalocephala bivalens,* for example) certain cells reputed to be germ cells are distinguishable during cleavage. They differ from somatic cells in cell and nuclear size (*Sphaerium*) as well as in behavior of their chromosomes (*Ascaris*).

In *Ascaris* during early cleavage stages, the chromosomes of the cells in the germ line behave in a manner which at superficial view would appear to be an almost graphic representation of the idea that germ cells retain the full complement of genetic factors, while somatic cell chromosomes suffer diminution. Beginning at second cleavage, the ends of the chromosomes are thrown off into the cytoplasm, where they disintegrate, while the middle parts of the chromosomes fragment into a number of pieces. One cell near the vegetal pole of the egg, however, retains chromosomes of the original shape, and gives rise to the germ cell line during later cleavage and development. Thus the nuclei of the germ line receive complete replicas of the chromosome materials of the zygote, while somatic cell nuclei suffer diminution.

Experiments are recorded in the literature that attribute these different kinds of chromosome behavior to differences in the cytoplasms in which presumptive germ cells and somatic cells find themselves. There is nothing to indicate, however, that the various *somatic* cell chromosomes differ among themselves in a manner conducive to the origin of different types of somatic cells.

All the above experiments indicate that unequivocal proof of germ cell determining plasms being passed from one generation to the next is not easily obtained. A hereditary continuity of which we may be certain belongs to the genes of the gamete chromosomes. This brings us now to the question of the manner in which the nucleus enters into the differentiation processes that occur during development.

5

Nuclear Equivalence
Versus Nuclear Differentiation

Weismann adopted the view that the specific character of a cell is determined by its nucleus. It was necessary to assume then that the various nuclei within the somatic cells of the developing embryo became different from one another. To explain the origin of these differences, he postulated what we now know to be an impossible type of chromosomal behavior at mitosis. As chromosome behavior during the mitotic cycle was described by the classical cytologists around the turn of this century, mitosis by definition involved an equal quantitative and qualitative "division" of chromosomes to be distributed to daughter cells. Later, crossing over between parts of homologous chromosomes during mitotic prophase was observed. This process, however, could not provide for the orderly sorting out of genes required in the Weismannian sense for cellular differentiation. The concept of unequal distribution of hereditary determinants during development was, however, subject to experimental test, and thus had an enormously stimulating effect upon other biologists (Reference 60 applies to the material in this chapter unless otherwise specified.)

SOME CLASSICAL EXPERIMENTS

Among the earliest experimental studies on the egg were those of Wilhelm Roux, whose first results were consistent with the theory of Weismann. When one of the first two blastomeres of a frog egg was pricked with a heated needle, it was killed. The remaining living half, however, went on to develop into a half embryo. Development of the living half proceeded while the lifeless half was still attached, and appeared to be entirely independent of the latter. Self-differentiation was the descriptive term introduced by Roux for this independent behavior. The living half under these experimental conditions behaved as though it contained determinants for one half embryo only, and it differentiated according to its self-contained capacities.

Ideally, however, for this experiment, complete separation of the blastomeres should be achieved. No means for doing this in the amphibian egg was as yet at hand. The same question therefore was put to the egg of the sea urchin, whose blastomeres could be separated by violent shaking, or later, more elegantly by placing early cleavage stages in calcium-free sea water. The intercellular "cement" of cells requires calcium for its integrity, and still today some methods of separating living cells depend upon removing the calcium by means of bonding or chelating agents such as versene (ethylene diamine tetraacetate).

The results of the early experiments made by Hans Driesch indicated that each of the first two blastomeres of the sea urchin egg *could* give rise to a half-sized but normal larva. This is not to say that the experiments gave positive results without exception. In one of the original reports by Driesch he states that 30 out of some 50 cases gave the small blastulae arising from cleavage of isolated first blastomeres, while the remaining ones either died or were sacrificed. One instance by chance repeated for the sea urchin precisely the condition achieved by Roux in the frog egg. That is, one of the first two blastomeres was killed and remained in close contact with the living, cleaving, remaining half. The living half went through cleavage impeded by the dead half. Then, unlike the frog egg, the living half began to invaginate, freed itself from the dead half, and later developed into a typical half-sized embryo.

Was there no underlying consistent pattern then in the development of various kinds of eggs? Such diametrically opposed results challenged the development of new techniques whereby the same question could be put to the amphibian egg in a more precise manner. It was found possible to constrict first the newt egg and later on Roux's own experimental material, the frog egg, at the two-cell stage. When a loop of hair or fine silk was tied around the two-celled embryo and its ends pulled to constrict the egg into its two blastomeres, *sometimes* two normally proportioned although half-sized embryos developed. Later on, the sporadic nature of this occurrence was traced to whether or not the future dorsal lip region (the gray crescent at the two-cell stage) of the embryo was distributed between both blastomeres (Fig. 6).

If the plane of first cleavage which separated the two blastomeres had been median (cutting through the gray crescent and dividing the right from the left half), then when entirely severed from one another by tightening the ligature, each blastomere formed a complete embryo. If the plane of first cleavage had been frontal (separating the future dorsal half from the ventral half), then the blastomere containing the gray crescent formed an embryo, while the other blastomere achieved cleavage and formation of three cell layers but no differentiation of organs (Fig. 7).

It was also found that a slight modification of Roux's method produced results with the frog egg that were consistent with those for the sea urchin. If, after pricking one of the first two blastomeres, the oper-

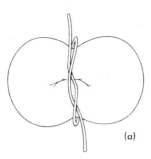 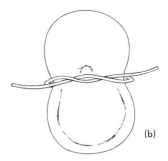

(a)   (b)

FIGURE 6. Two gastrulae of a newt illustrating different planes of ligature with respect to position of the dorsal lip. The ligatures had been made at the two-cell stage when plane of cleavage or position of the gray crescent are the only markers for the future dorso-ventral axis of the embryo. Ligature (a) resulted in development of two small, normal embryos. In (b) only the half including the dorsal lip developed. (After Spemann, 1938.)

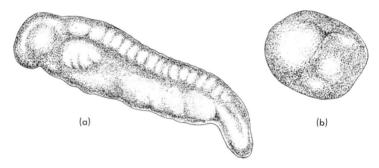

(a)   (b)

FIGURE 7. Results of tight frontal ligature of the fertilized egg when the two halves had been completely separated. The dorsal half (a) containing the gray crescent formed a well-proportioned embryo. (After Spemann, 1938.)

ator kept the egg in an inverted position, the surviving blastomere developed into a whole although half-sized frog embryo. Thus the original pricking experiments had not revealed the true potencies of the half egg. Once again we must note that the validity of an observation, a "fact," depends upon and is qualified by the experimental method used to ask a question of a living organism.

THE GRAY CRESCENT AND ITS IMPLICATIONS FOR THE PROBLEM

The inversion experiment further suggested the importance of contact among various components of the egg cytoplasm. In the heavily yolked amphibian egg, these components are to a large extent distributed according to their specific gravities. The rotation movements that follow fertilization bring about new contacts between various types of cytoplasmic components, some of which are localized in the egg cortex. Inversion of the egg or mild centrifugation also bring about such new contacts. The original pricking experiments could not be interpreted simply as mechanical interference by the dead blastomere, for inversion could not then alleviate the deficiency. The dead blastomere still exerted pressure upon the living one. Thus regulation toward wholeness after inversion is presumed to result from the establishment of contacts between the various internal and cortical cytoplasmic components.

That the components involved may be of surface (cortical) and internal derivation respectively is suggested by another example of the developmental significance of contact relationships. Let us look for a moment at the normal rotation movements which follow activation or fertilization of the amphibian egg. Through rotation of the egg, the position of the gray crescent is established. Hence at this time the location of the future dorsal lip of the blastopore and the determination of the dorso-ventral axis of the embryo come about.

Ovarian eggs already possess one axis whose opposite ends are called respectively the animal and vegetal poles. This animal-vegetal axis results from the pattern of storage of reserve materials within the growing oocytes in the ovary of the female. The vegetal pole is thus designated as that end of the egg axis whose cytoplasm contains the highest concentration of yolk materials in the form of yolk platelets containing phosphoprotein, sulfoprotein, lipoprotein, nucleic acid, and polysaccharide. These materials grade off as one proceeds to measure them at levels extending from vegetal toward animal poles. The opposing animal-vegetal axis is characterized by a higher concentration at the animal pole of "active" cytoplasm—smaller granular constituents, higher content of respiratory enzymes, ribonucleic acids, and so on.

When the eggs are laid, one finds them with random orientations with respect to the animal-vegetal axis. Thus some eggs quite by chance will be oriented according to gravity, with the heavier vegetal pole downward and animal pole up. In most eggs, however, the axis will be at some angle to the gravitational field, or even directly opposing it, with the heavy vegetal pole up. The eggs at this time are tightly encased in the vitelline membrane and cannot rotate. Upon activation or fertilization, the membrane lifts or is forced from the egg surface, leaving a fluid-filled space (the perivitelline space) within which now the egg is free to rotate in accordance with the field of gravity.

The meridian through which rotation occurs in those eggs laid with vegetal poles initially pointing upward has been shown to determine the location of the gray crescent [12]. Thus the gray crescent forms on the side along which the vegetal pole descended (Fig. 8). Some of the pigmented cortex of the egg is dragged along and toward the interior of the egg with the rotation movement. If an egg is laid with the animal pole by chance pointing upward, then the gray crescent forms preferably at the side of the egg opposite that where the sperm enters.

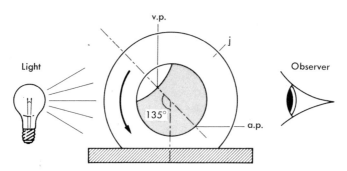

FIGURE 8. Formation of the gray crescent with respect to rotation of the fertilized frog egg. Vegetal pole (v.p.), animal pole (a.p.), jelly (j). The gray crescent forms on the side along which the vegetal pole descends. (After Ancel and Vintemberger 1948, in Brachet, 1957.)

The cortical reaction set up as a result of sperm penetration can therefore also bring about the mixing of plasms of which the gray crescent is the visible symptom. That the role of the sperm is secondary, however, is shown by the fact that if an unfertilized egg is fixed in place so that its animal pole points upward, and then is activated by means of an electrical induction shock instead of by normal sperm penetration, then the gray crescent may be formed anywhere along the marginal zone between yolk and pigmented hemispheres.

Some recent experiments [22] indicate that the special properties of the gray crescent region are localized in its cortical portion. Minute pieces of the cortex of the gray crescent grafted into another egg induce a secondary embryo in the latter.

Thus the conclusion was reached that profound effects upon development are brought about by initially cytoplasmic, not nuclear, factors, and that the first two nuclei of the cleaving egg are alike in their abilities to support the complete development of a normal embryo. The road thus was indicated for still further experiments on early amphibian embryos, and ingenious techniques gradually multiplied as the question of equivalence of early cleavage nuclei was pursued. The constriction technique was elaborated and extended in the delayed nucleation experiments next to be described.

LIGATURING THE EGG: DELAYED NUCLEATION

These experiments were devised to find out whether even later derivatives of the zygote nucleus could support the full range of differentiation potencies of the egg. Shortly after fertilization, a ligature of human hair could be tied around the newt egg and its membranes, as mentioned above. The ligature could be kept relatively loose or tightened to a degree such that the egg was almost cut into two parts. Since the technique requires much skill, each constriction attempted did not meet the criteria for a critical experiment. Only those experimental individuals were followed up in which (1) both parts after constriction were of almost equal size (quantity of cytoplasm the constant, proportion of original zygote nucleus the variable), and (2) the protective membranes around the egg were undamaged.

Depending upon the tightness of the ligature, one part of the egg remained anucleate for a period of time during which the other half within which the zygote nucleus had been trapped proceeded to cleave. Sooner or later a descendant of the zygote nucleus would wander across the cytoplasmic bridge and initiate cleavage in the previously anucleate "half." Sometimes this occurred after only two cleavages; in other cases, four or five cleavages had occurred before a nucleus found its way across the bridge.

Two classes of results were obtained, as indicated in Fig. 9. From some ligatured eggs, the part that contained three of the four nuclei resulting during the first two cleavages continued to segment but failed to differentiate. This part became separated from the other half and formed a well-rounded ball of cells. The other part, which contained only one of the first four cleavage nuclei (and that only after some delay), formed a normal embryo. Thus quantity of nuclear material failed to account for failure to differentiate.

Another class of results gave twins developing from both parts of an egg ligatured in such a way that one part remained anucleate while the other part segmented into sixteen cells. When finally one of these sixteen nuclei found its way into the uncleaved part, division began here also. The age difference persisted for a long time, but eventually (140 days) became obliterated. The twins appeared alike in their differentiation despite the fact that one developed from only "one-sixteenth" of the original zygote nucleus. When cleavage in one half had reached the 32-cell stage, however, passage of one of these nuclei into the other half failed to promote normal development of the egg fragment.

Now as to interpretation, first of all these experimental results certainly are at variance with predictions from Weismannian theory, according to which a "one-sixteenth nucleus" already would have suffered restriction as to types of differentiations it can support. Secondly, since

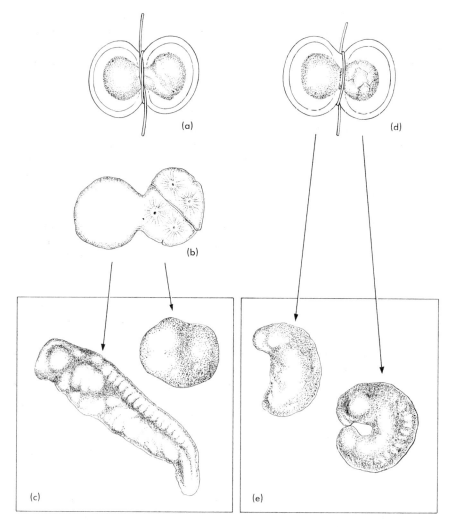

Figure 9. Delayed nucleation experiment: a test for nuclear equivalence during early cleavage. (a) The newt egg constricted by a hair loop after fertilization but before first cleavage, shown here at the two-cell stage; the zygote nucleus was confined by constriction to the right half. (b) Section through constricted egg now at the four-cell stage. The nucleus nearest the "bridge" between the two halves of the egg is about to migrate into the uncleaved half. (c) Developmental results in the two halves: the part that contained only one of the first four cleavage nuclei after tight constriction formed a normal embryo. (d) Anucleate half of constricted egg has belatedly received a descendant of the zygote nucleus at the sixteen-cell stage. (e) Developmental results in the two halves: twins were produced showing at first an age difference, later obliterated, due to the delay in cleavage in the previously anucleate half. (Modified from Spemann, 1938.)

quantity of nuclear material does not here determine the outcome, whether development of an egg fragment will occur depends upon the quality of the cytoplasm and not the nucleus.

When early gastrula stages were similarly ligatured, the same two general classes of results were observed: one normal embryo with one cleaved but undifferentiated half, or two half-sized but normal twin embryos. The former resulted after ligatures that separated the half of the egg containing the dorsal lip from the ventral half (frontal plane ligatures). The twin embryos resulted from ligatures tied in the median plane such that each half of the young gastrula contained a part of the dorsal lip. The dorsal lip served as a convenient marker for orientation of the ligature.

As further experiments came to show, the dorsal lip forms in the region of the gray crescent, which as we have noted earlier, appears shortly after fertilization. In the early constriction experiments, therefore, a satisfactory explanation of the two classes of results would depend upon the plane of ligature with respect to the gray crescent. Thus cytoplasmic, not nuclear, inequalities were implicated in differentiation of the embryo. And here began the schism between experimental embryologists and geneticists which persisted for several generations, until at last it became apparent that neither nucleus nor cytoplasm alone leads an autonomous existence but that they interdepend in a manner most significant for normal development.

Let us reexamine some of the ligature experiments in which nucleation of one half was delayed until cleavage had proceeded to the sixteen-cell stage in the other half. As mentioned above, in some experiments a "one-sixteenth zygote nucleus" gave as good differentiation as "fifteen-sixteenths" of a zygote nucleus—or the entire zygote nucleus, for that matter. In other ligatured eggs, however, a "one-sixteenth" nucleus gave differentiation that stopped altogether at late gastrula or early neurula stage. These two classes of results again were correlated with the plane in which the ligature divided the cytoplasm. But some new information came to light [39].

If the ligature had separated future right and left sides of the embryo, a one-sixteenth (but not a one-thirty second) zygote nucleus could promote normal differentiation when it wandered into the opposite lateral half. If, on the other hand, the one-sixteenth nucleus was derived from cleavage in the *ventral* half, it could *not* support differentiation in the dorsal half of the egg when permitted to wander across. What was the lack in this latter case? Cytoplasmic, to be sure—but directly or indirectly?

Here we must correct and depart from the outmoded idea that the zygote nucleus "divides" into more and more parts during cleavage, an idea implicit in terms such as "one-sixteenth zygote nucleus." During interphase, the chromosomes form replicas of themselves after separation of their component strands. The raw materials for replication must be at hand, with ultimately the cytoplasm as the source of supply for the amino acids, energy sources, and the components of nucleic acids required for chromosome replication.

Two interpretations of the failure of a "one-sixteenth nucleus" always to promote development may be suggested. (1) A nucleus resulting from chromosome replication in the ventral half found inadequate precursors to form complete and normal replicas of its chromosomes. A nucleus replicating in a lateral half found an array of precursors, including perhaps gray crescent derivatives, qualitatively and quantitatively adequate to support the synthesis of normal chromosomes. (2) From an alternative viewpoint, however, it could be maintained that chromosome replication proceeded normally to the sixteen-cell stage in the ventral half of the ligatured embryo, but that the anucleate dorsal cytoplasm deteriorated for lack of nuclear materials and could not thereafter respond fully to the stimulus of the one-sixteenth nucleus that finally arrived. As it has been differently stated: "The susceptibility of the cytoplasm of a dorsal half is greater than that of a lateral half . . . ; accordingly the latter can survive absence of a nucleus during the time required for the zygote nucleus to divide four times, while the former loses its capacity for complete development if it has remained enucleate for a longer time than that required for three divisions of the zygote nucleus" [39, p. 88].

What experiments might be set up to decide between these alternatives? Can we provide a one-sixteenth nucleus with cytoplasm known to be able to support normal development? In theory, yes; by enucleating the activated egg and injecting the test nucleus. For this hypothetical experiment, normal development provides the only control needed. The cytoplasm of the egg contains all the components necessary for normal development following fertilization and fusion of male and female pronuclei to form the zygote nucleus. In a later chapter we will discuss more recent experiments concerned with the problem of nuclear equivalence versus nuclear differentiation.

In the light of our expanding understanding of the nature of chromosome replication, it is not impossible that the chromosomes replicating in ventral cytoplasm themselves become deficient. Compare, for example, the studies of chromosome replication by *Rana pipiens* chromosomes which have been transplanted into *Rana sylvatica* cytoplasm by injecting a blastula nucleus of the former into an enucleated ovum of the latter. Moore and others have found that after a number of replications in the foreign species cytoplasm, the *pipiens* have been altered so that when a derived or daughter nucleus is back-transferred into an enucleated *pipiens* egg, the altered *pipiens* chromosomes cannot function to produce normal development in what originally was their own type of cytoplasm [49].

Thus the character of the nucleus is subject to cytoplasmic influence as well as the converse. In any event, the classical delayed nucleation experiments were not compatible with the nonequivalence demanded by Weismann's theory for the character of early cleavage nuclei.

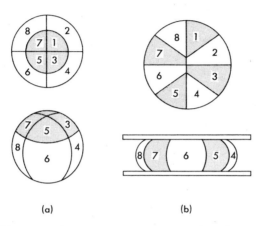

(a)   (b)

FIGURE 10. Diagrammatic representation of position of blastomeres in normal cleavage (a), and in eggs submitted to pressure during the first three cleavages into eight cells (b). Nuclei are not shown in the diagram but it is obvious that the daughter nuclei of eggs cleaving under pressure will be positioned in areas of cytoplasm different from those in which they normally are located. (After Huxley and de Beer, 1934.)

COMPRESSION EXPERIMENTS

Still another corollary of this theory was subjected to experimental test. If, during cleavage, nuclei could be forced into areas of cytoplasm not normally their habitat, and if these nuclei undergo "segregation of determinants," the various regions of the embryo would develop in abnormal spatial relationships one to the other. An experimental method designed to explore this hypothesis involved compressing the cleaving egg between glass plates, thereby mechanically forcing the third cleavage furrow (normally horizontal) to form vertical to the plane of compression [39]. At the eight-cell stage, the pressure could be released and subsequent development observed (Fig. 10). Development was normal in spite of the fact that many of the daughter nuclei perforce were relocated in areas of cytoplasm different from those in which they normally would be located.

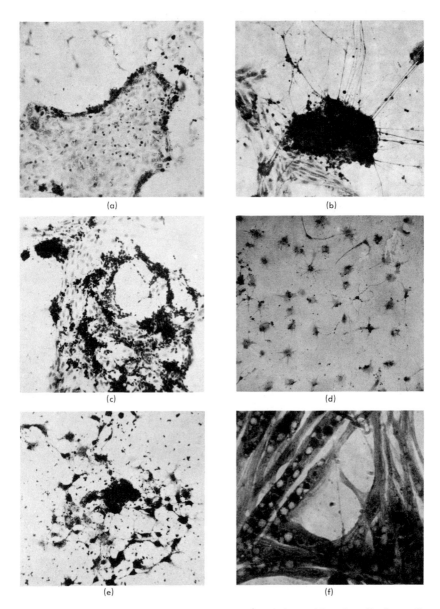

FIGURE 11. Developmental capacities of presumptive epidermis cells from the frog egg at early gastrula stage as revealed by treatment with lithium chloride and culture *in vitro*. (a) Control, untreated cells in a sheet of epithelium attached to the glass surface of the dish. (b) Mass of neuroblasts with nerve fibers radiating outward typical of presumptive epidermis cells treated for a brief period or at a relatively low concentration of lithium. (c) A different type of nerve pattern induced by lithium; mass of neuroblasts breaks up and spreads as clumps and

MULTIPLE POTENCIES IN EARLY DEVELOPMENT

Another necessary deduction from a Weismannian type of theory would be the rapid restriction of developmental capacities of the various regions of the egg as determinants for differentiation are parcelled out by means of qualitatively unequal nuclear divisions. The techniques of transplantation and explantation developed by the Spemann school, and presently still widely in use, have given many examples of the multiple potencies of various embryonic areas [38]. Far from being rigidly limited as to developmental capacities, various regions of the early amphibian embryo can be led to exhibit an amazing range of potencies under experimental conditions. Isolation, transplantation, and defect experiments, as well as the external application of chemical agents, have provided proof that even as late as the beginning of gastrulation when the first patterning of egg organization into presumptive areas can be demonstrated, the various presumptive regions still show a wide range of developmental capacities.

For example, when the small area of the early gastrula that normally would form only muscle (somites) is cut out and cultured in a physiological salt solution, it may organize itself into a patterned system of tissues containing notochord, spinal cord with anterior brainlike enlargement, and bilaterally oriented young muscle cells (myoblasts). Similarly, a bit of presumptive notochord in isolation will form not only notochord but also somites and even neural and epidermal structures.

The presumptive epidermis of the early gastrula forms merely epidermal cells *in vitro*, but it will respond to chemical agents added to the medium and reveal a wide range of potencies. In our own laboratory, for example, after adding a simple inorganic salt, lithium chloride, to the medium in which small aggregates of presumptive epidermis cells are being cultured, we observe [5] conversion of the cells into several types of nerve cells, pigment cells, mesenchyme cells, neuroglia cells, and occasionally even muscle cells (Fig. 11). And, of course, presumptive epidermis will respond to living or killed tissues from many sources to form an entire secondary embryo or a chimera of nerve, sense organs, notochord, muscle, and so on.

Another example of the remarkable potencies of the young presumptive epidermis and presumptive neural plate was obtained by transplant-

---

as individual neuroblasts. (d) Pigment cells induced from presumptive epidermis by more intense lithium treatment. (e) After still longer lithium treatment, cells resembling neuroglia differentiate. (f) Muscle cells may develop from presumptive epidermis. The photograph of muscle cells was made at a higher magnification than that used for parts (a) through (e). (Data from Barth and Barth, 1963; photographs previously unpublished.)

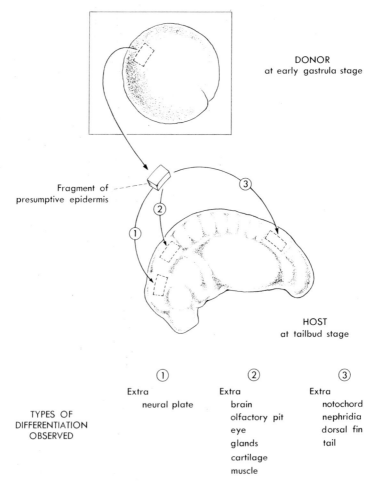

FIGURE 12. Some potencies of the presumptive epidermis of the young gastrula as demonstrated by transplantation into an older host at three antero-posterior levels. (Drawn from Spemann's description of experiments by J. Holtfreter, page 290, in Spemann, 1938.)

ing pieces from either of these regions from an early gastrula into the lateral region at the side of the nerve cord of an older embryo (Fig. 12). These transplants of young epidermis healed in and later, when the host was sectioned, the transplants were found to contain accessory organs of all kinds corresponding to the region of the host. Thus in the region of the host's head, an extra neural plate formed on a gill arch. A little more posteriorly at the level of the auditory vesicle the transplant formed brain with olfactory pit and an eye with lens, as well as glands, mesenchyme, cartilage, and muscle. In the trunk region of the host, the transplants formed notochord, nephridia, dorsal fin, and tail.

Such transplantation experiments point up the effect of the immediate environment upon expression of the potencies of cells and suggest a certain amount of specificity in such environmental effects. The antero-posterior level in which the transplant finds itself affects the type of differentiation achieved. In the present context, the experiments provide another piece of evidence that at the early gastrula stage at least, there has been no restrictive segregation of determinants, genes, in the cells destined in later normal development to form epidermal or neural structures. Whatever "determination" has occurred is admittedly subject to alternative pathways, and thus cannot represent irreversible genetic restriction among nuclei in the Weismannian sense.

GENETIC FACTORS AND EMBRYONIC INDUCTION

The experiments cited thus far would appear to indicate that developmental processes are under cytoplasmic and environmental control exclusively. This is by no means the case even for early steps in development, as we shall discuss in the following chapter. Meanwhile let us examine two classical experiments which illustrate the intervention of genes at somewhat *later* stages of development.

In the first experiment, the factors involved in development of some head structures were examined. Among the tailless amphibians (urodeles) *Triton* normally develops ventrocaudal to the eyes a pair of long club-shaped filaments called balancers, which serve to attach and support the larva. Other urodeles (axolotl, for example) do not develop these structures. Even in *Triton*, however, balancers will not develop unless the presumptive balancer tissue is in a position where it will receive its cue from the appropriate adjacent tissues. That is, balancers will not self-differentiate; they require an inductor.

This can be shown by transplanting the presumptive balancer epidermis from a young neurula into either (1) the trunk region of a somewhat older larva, or (2) blastocoele of an early gastrula. In these foreign loci lacking the normal mesodermal inductors balancers fail to develop (Table 1).

On the other hand, it can be shown that even though axolotl does not form a balancer, it can provide the inductors for a balancer. Trunk epidermis from an early neurula of *Triton* was moved into the lateral

facial region of a young axolotl neurula. This epidermis formed a fine
balancer under the influence of factors present in the head region of the
axolotl host. Since the balancer of *Triton* cannot self-differentiate, it
follows that axolotl provided the inductors—although itself being unresponsive to them. In the reciprocal experiment, presumptive epidermis
from an early gastrula of axolotl was implanted into the presumptive
face region of a *Triton* gastrula. Although several head structures developed (lens, gills, and ears) no balancer was formed. Thus axolotl
epidermis responds neither to its own inductors nor to those of a host
(Table 1). The differences between these two groups of amphibians are
of course genetically determined. These experiments indicate that among
the gene-determined differences ability to respond (competence) to a
specific inductor must be included.

TABLE 1

Normal development	P.b. in abnormal location	Transplantation results	
Triton +	—	P. ep. T into A_f	+
Axolotl −	—	P. ep. A into T_f	−

Code: T = *Triton;* A = axolotl; + = balancer present; − =
balancer absent; f = facial region; P. ep. = presumptive epidermis; P. b. = presumptive balancer.
Compiled from Spemann [60].

Further striking results were observed when exchanges were made between urodele and anuran gastrula ectoderm. The anuran (frog) larva
forms mucus-secreting glands (suckers) instead of balancers. Both
suckers and balancers are head structures, but they occupy different
positions on the heads of the frog and the newt respectively. Presumptive
belly epidermis from the early frog gastrula was grafted into the future
head region of a newt early gastrula with the result shown in Fig. 13.
The host newt developed suckers in the location appropriate for frog
suckers. The reciprocal operation gave rise to a frog larva with balancers. In one interesting case (not diagrammed) the transplant consisted of a small piece of frog epidermis that came to lie in a median
position, leaving free and untouched the more anteriorly located regions
of the host newt's head. Here then the host developed balancers as
usual from its own tissues and also induced suckers from the transplanted
frog epidermis (O. Schotté in Spemann, 1938, ref. 60). Here again presumably it is the genes that determine the precise character of a developing structure.

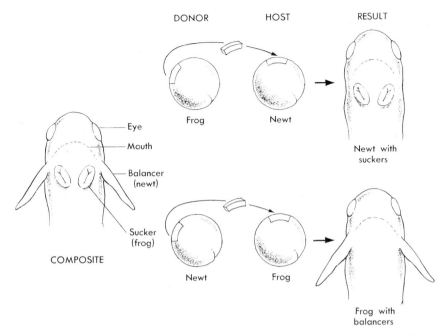

FIGURE 13. Induction of head structures in grafts between two kinds of amphibians. On the left is a composite view to show the relative positions on the ventral side of the head of balancers (characteristic of newt tadpoles) and of suckers (found in frog tadpoles). The middle diagrams show presumptive epidermis removed from one type of early gastrula and grafted into the future head region of the other kind of amphibian at early gastrula stage. Developmental results are indicated on the right. (After Schotté in Spemann, 1938.)

More precise demonstration of genetic factors in development can be drawn from the study of mutant pure strains of the house mouse, where the genotype of a given individual is known. One famous example concerns the "short-tail" locus. Mice homozygous for this gene have no tails, no rectum, anus, urethra, or genital papilla. They die at birth if not earlier. Heterozygotes for "short-tail" show varying degrees of reduction in size of their kidneys and ureters, and sometimes even complete absence of these structures [35]. A careful analysis of these abnormal mice revealed that kidney tissues never formed unless a ureter grew out and made contact with the presumptive kidney tissues (Fig. 14). One of the effects of the mutant gene was to interfere with the normal elongation and branching of the bud from the mesonephric duct which develops into ureter normally. Thus, another example is provided of a developmental effect with a gene-controlled cause.

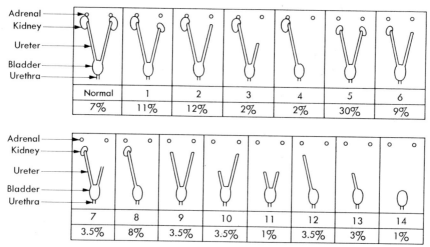

Frequency of malformations among 109 individuals

Figure 14. Urogenital structures of the normal house mouse and malformations observed in newborn mice heterozygous for short-tail and taillessness. The gene mutation interfered to varying degrees with a developmental event necessary for induction of kidney development. Outgrowth of the mesonephric duct which normally develops into the ureter is interfered with in many of the heterozygotes. (From Gluecksohn-Schoenheimer in Grüneberg, 1943.)

To sum up, the experiments cited in this chapter have disposed of the original "Weismann-Roux theory" in its original form. We may not, however, discount the role of genetic control of early developmental processes. The following chapters will examine the effects upon *early* development of interferences with the quantity and quality of nuclear materials.

6

Quantity of Nuclear Materials
as a Factor in Development

THE UNFERTILIZED OVUM AS A DIFFERENTIATED CELL

Nothing about the structure or metabolism of a mature ovum furnishes any indication of the immanence of an adult organism. No outstanding peculiarities in chemical composition or metabolism distinguish the egg from all other cells. The amphibian egg is rich in yolk (in the form of platelets, Fig. 15), but some eggs contain relatively more yolk (fish and avian eggs) and others (mammalian eggs) relatively less. Thus yolk content is more reasonably considered as an adaptive feature associated with the environment in which development will occur. Mammalian embryos obtain their energy largely from materials supplied by the placenta. Adult differentiated cells, such as liver and muscle cells, contain relatively copious amounts of glycogen, representing stored potential energy reserves. One cannot, therefore, even single out high content of stored nutriments as a distinguishing characteristic of the ovum as compared with other cells.

The unfertilized egg consumes oxygen and eliminates carbon dioxide at a low but measurable rate that increases (in amphibia) at fertilization and continues to rise with further development. The energy of oxidation is coupled with developmental processes through energy-rich bonds in the form of adenosine triphosphate (ATP)—again a common feature of other cells in both plant and animal kingdom [for references see 12, 13, 45].

The cytoplasm of the ovum is rich in ribonucleic acid (RNA), which compound is known to play a major role in protein synthesis in many kinds of cells (gland cells, microorganisms, as well as embryos). Much of this RNA is associated with cytoplasmic granules, which are present in larger quantities in the amphibian egg at the animal pole than at the vegetal pole. The endoplasmic reticulum characteristic of adult cells such as liver and kidney is simpler in an ovum. The mitochondria (granules containing important respiratory enzymes) are simpler in structure and enzyme activity in the oocyte than in differentiated cells. The surface of the amphibian oocyte, viewed by means of the electron

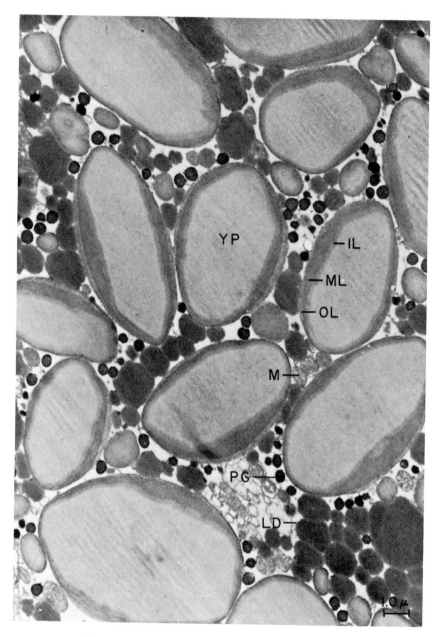

FIGURE 15. Electron microscope photograph of a section through a mature frog egg 1 mm in diameter. Yolk platelets (YP), pigment granules (PG), mitochondria (M), and lipid droplets (LD) are shown. (From Ward, 1962.)

microscope, shows micro-villi and cortical granules and thus exhibits greater structural complexity than the interior [42]. But altogether, the structure (Fig. 16) and chemical composition of the cytoplasm of the ovum are deceptively simple and not unique in quality.

The quantitative distribution of the various components does vary between the different regions of the egg. This is especially clear in the amphibian egg, and a number of studies have been made of chemical composition and metabolic activity of the various regions of the early gastrula [for references see 4]. Some biologists have attributed differentiation entirely to the localization of blastomere nuclei in the regionally different ooplasms that arose during growth of the egg in the ovary. The problem of development thus would be relegated to the previous generation, the idea being that previous cytoplasmic differentiation is the decisive guide for the specific synthetic activities that lead to the origin of new cell types and ultimately differentiated tissues and organs. The role of the nucleus in development then would be primarily in bringing about these cytoplasmic differences while the egg is maturing in the ovary during the process of oogenesis.

To use the frog egg again as our example, the mature frog oocyte is the product of three years of growth in the ovary of the female. Glycogen, phospholipids, lipids, phosphoproteins, and proteins accumulate during the growth period [32]. These compounds are stored in the several types of granular, membranous, and droplet structures of the cytoplasm. And, as we have noted above, these structures are not homogeneously distributed throughout the egg, but rather, asymmetrically and in more or less polarized fashion. There is little doubt that genetic mechanisms determine which substances are synthesized and, at least indirectly, their patterns of distribution in the cytoplasm.

While thus admitting that the nucleus already has mediated in laying down the basic pattern of egg organization and that this pattern is bound to play a role in *normal* development in some kinds of eggs, let us realize that very little of cause-effect relationships is revealed simply by observing normal development. Such "molecular preformation" does indeed exist in some eggs. Let us remember, however, that early developments in many eggs is highly labile. The cytoplasmic (molecular) pattern may be profoundly altered by experimental means, yet the embryo in many instances will accommodate itself to the new artificial pattern and proceed to develop.

As we noted in an earlier chapter, even such a fundamental property as orientation of the dorso-ventral axis is subject to experimental intervention. Any area around the marginal zone between yolk and pigmented hemispheres is potentially the gray crescent or future notochord region. The actual position at which the gray crescent forms usually is

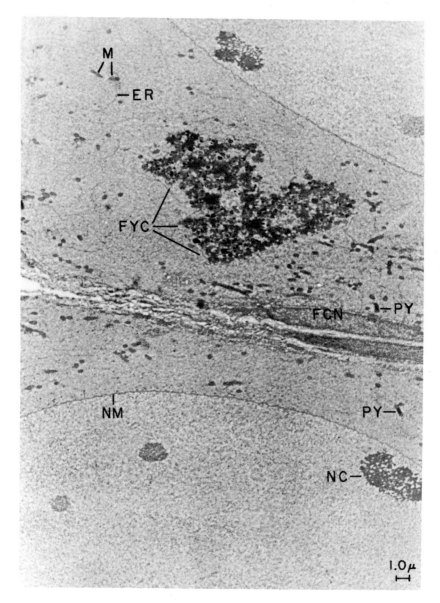

FIGURE 16. Electron microscope photograph of a section through two adjacent oocytes of the frog tadpole ovary. Abbreviations pertinent to the present text include: ER, endoplasmic reticulum; M, mitochondria; NC, nucleolus; NM, nuclear membrane. (From Ward, 1962.)

determined by the chance factor of direction of rotation in the activated ovum. Twin embryos may be produced by separation of blastomeres or halves of young gastrulae. Double-sized giant embryos may be manufactured by fusion of two eggs at the two-cell stage. Embryos with more than one nerve axis can result from centrifugation or after transplantation of accessory presumptive notochord regions in the early gastrula stage. These are some of the unique developmental phenomena which have the deepest interest for the experimental biologist.

Having taken note of the role of the nucleus in the preparatory phases of oogenesis, let us go on now to some of the facts known about nuclear effects upon developmental processes *per se*.

Effect on Development of Absence of a Nucleus

In the eggs of both sea urchins and amphibians, cleavage and partial blastula formation occur in the absence of the nucleus, but the eggs block before gastrulation. One method used to produce achromosomal embryos (or rather, eggs lacking functional chromosomes) is so ingenious and convincing as to merit description [16].

A frog egg is fertilized with X-irradiated sperm, after which the egg nucleus is removed by means of a microneedle. The chromosomes of the irradiated sperm nucleus degenerate, but the sperm aster functions to contribute to formation of the mitotic apparatus. Such eggs go through early cleavage at a somewhat retarded rate, until a partial blastula is formed with cells restricted to part of the animal hemisphere plus a portion of the upper vegetal hemisphere on one side of the egg. Proof that the chromosomes actually were effectively destroyed as to function came from the use of eggs and sperm from two different species.

This hybrid consisted of eggs of *Rana pipiens* (Vermont leopard frog) and sperm from *Rana catesbeiana* (New Jersey bullfrog). As indicated in Fig. 17, (1) a normal *R. pipiens* egg fertilized by a normal nonirradiated *catesbeiana* sperm develops until early gastrula stage, at which time it blocks and later dies; (2) a normal *R. pipiens* egg fertilized by an irradiated *catesbeiana* sperm develops to a post-neurula stage (with certain abnormalities, classified as the haploid syndrome, that later lead to death), but it does develop beyond the gastrula stage; (3) a *Rana pipiens* egg fertilized with *catesbeiana* sperm previously exposed to the same dose of X-irradiation used in set (2) and then subjected to removal of its egg nucleus exhibits only retarded and partial cleavage.

If removal of the *pipiens* nucleus had failed, a tadpole exhibiting the haploid syndrome would have formed in (3). If the sperm irradiation had been inadequate, a haploid embryo whose chromosomes were derived from *catesbeiana* and whose cytoplasm was *pipiens* in character would

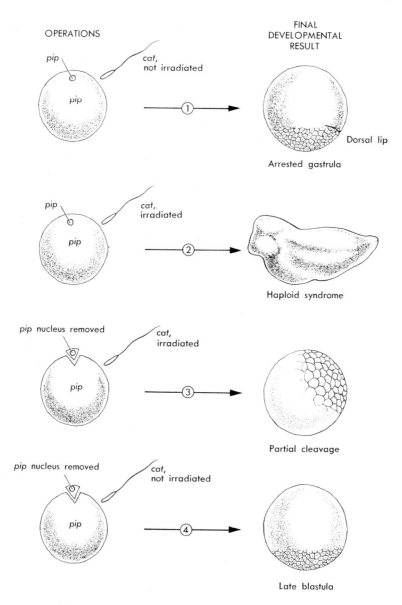

FIGURE 17. Schematic representation of proof for production of "achromosomal" embryos lacking functional chromosomes. The species of eggs and sperm used were *Rana catesbeiana* (*cat*) and *Rana pipiens* (*pip*). (Drawn from Briggs *et al*, 1951).

have been produced. Such an egg completes cleavage and blastula formation, although it blocks before a dorsal lip can be formed (4). Thus a beautifully controlled experiment demonstrates the necessity for at least one set of intact chromosomes for even the early stages of development.

Haploidy

The experimental production of an egg with only one set of chromosomes permits development into a young larva with a characteristic syndrome of abnormalities that lead eventually to death. Whether the single set of chromosomes is of maternal or paternal origin does not significantly affect the result. The abnormalities reported include a subnormal archenteron (primitive gut); microcephaly; short, broad body; deficiencies in blood circulation; reduced motility and reactivity; and most obviously, pronounced edema (although this condition may result from many causes other than haploidy). Most haploid embryos die before the feeding stage.

The classical method for producing haploid amphibian larvae was to activate the egg without fertilization by pricking with a needle dipped in blood. Pricking with a clean needle causes lifting of the fertilization membrane and rotation of the egg. The second maturation spindle now is located at the animal pole. No further development ensues. When the necessity for a "second factor" for cleavage initiation was recognized in the early 1900's it was thought that the nucleus of a blood cell contained some cleavage-initiating substance. In fact, one investigator claimed that only white blood cells contained the parthenogenetic agent, because a needle dipped into either whole blood or into lymph provided the stimulus for cleavage—and white blood cells are common to both these body fluids! You will have little difficulty in criticizing this conclusion, which actually was published. More recent work has shown that the common parthenogenetic agent (cleavage-initiating material) is more probably located in cytoplasmic granules (microsomes, but especially mitochondria), both of which produce parthenogenetic development subsequent to their injection into the virgin egg [55].

From the discussion of methods of producing achromosomal embryos discussed above, two further methods of inducing haploid development will occur to you. Gynogenesis is achieved when eggs are fertilized with sperm previously inactivated with X-ray treatment or with dyes (toluidine blue, for example) that destroy the integrity of the chromatin without affecting the sperm aster needed to contribute to the achromatic mitotic apparatus required for cytoplasmic division. Androgenesis is achieved when, after fertilization with normal sperm, the egg nucleus is removed by means of a glass microneedle.

The reason for lethality in the haploid condition is still unknown. One hypothesis attributes the poor development to the abnormally low nucleocytoplasmic ratio, which is supposed in some manner to impede proper utilization of yolk reserves for developmental purposes. Haploids from large eggs show more severe effects than haploids from small eggs. A single clutch of frog embryos may show variations in volume ratios of as much as 1.73 to 1.00 [15].

Another interpretation maintains that a lethal gene (or genes), masked in the diploid condition, is (are) "unmasked" in the haploid state. Every gamete, egg or sperm, would have to contain this lethal gene, since no haploid ever survives. Considered as a Mendelian recessive, this gene should be present in a wildtype population of frogs so that in every egg clutch one-quarter of the fertilized eggs should be homozygous for the lethal condition. In actual practice in the laboratory, a careful investigator routinely obtains 99 to 100% fertilization and normal development. Furthermore, when a haploid "regulates" to the diploid condition, as sometimes occurs when one of the early nuclear divisions is not followed by a cytoplasmic division, one would expect a homozygous lethal condition. The opposite is the case; development can be normal in this situation.

Polyploidy and Aneuploidy [27]

Continuing our analysis of effects of quantitative variations in nuclear materials, polyploidy alters the nucleocytoplasmic ratio to excess of the normal diploid condition. Chemical agents that injure the mitotic apparatus (spindle and asters) sometimes result in polyploidy. Such compounds as mercaptoethanol, colchicine, nitrogen mustards, and the enzyme ribonuclease have this effect. More reliable methods consist of exposing newly fertilized eggs either to refrigeration for several hours or to supranormal temperatures (36°C) for ten minutes. These experimental methods, as well as spontaneously occurring accidents in meiosis, lead to retention of the second polar body of the egg, which latter after fertilization therefore contains two haploid sets of maternal chromosomes plus one set of paternal chromosomes. In addition to such triploids, tetraploid and pentaploid larvae of spontaneous origin sometimes are found (less than 0.5% of wild population in nature).

Development of polyploids is normal. The larvae hatch and continue to grow. Their overall body size also is normal. They contain fewer but larger cells than their diploid counterparts. Nuclear volume is approximately proportional to number of chromosome sets, and the cytoplasmic volume regulates upward to accommodate the larger nucleus.

Although possession of entire extra chromosome sets thus has no unfavorable effect upon development, possession of unbalanced, partial extra sets does. Such aneuploid embryos may be produced by mating a triploid female with a diploid male. At the first meiotic division, while the egg is en route to the oviduct, the third set of maternal chromosomes is distributed at random between the two poles of the spindle. The resulting eggs range from a haploid number to almost a diploid condition. Viability in such aneuploids is greatly reduced, possibly as a result of circulatory defects in the young larvae.

To summarize the effects of quantitative variations of nuclear materials upon differentiation: Normal development requires a certain minimum of nuclear material. Development can proceed normally with excess gene sets if all the chromosomes are equally represented in the polyploid. We are therefore supplied with further evidence for participation of the nucleus in differentiation. The effects of quantitative differences in nuclear materials, however, shed little light upon the manner in which genetic factors affect *specific* developmental processes.

7

The Problem of Nuclear Differentiation

In pursuing the problem of whether nuclei undergo *qualitative* changes
—temporary or permanent—during development and to what extent the
quality of nuclear materials affects development, two principal lines of
experimentation will be described in this and the following chapter.
These will be (1) nuclear transplantation studies and (2) work with interspecies hybrids.

EVIDENCE FROM DESCRIPTIVE STUDIES

Insofar as nuclear differentiation is concerned, there is presumptive
evidence on the affirmative side from the *appearance* of nuclei in various
cells and in the same cell type during different phases of activity. The
gross appearance of nuclei (size, shape, size of nucleoli, and so on) differs
markedly among various kinds of differentiated cells. Nuclei also vary
in their specific protein and enzyme contents where these have been analyzed. The bird erythrocyte nucleus contains hemoglobin. Mammalian
liver cell nuclei have high arginase content, while bird kidney nuclei are
low in this enzyme [47, p. 97]. Glycogen is found in the liver cell nuclei
of the amphibian tadpole [37]. Such variations may be end results of
differentiation. Certainly they furnish no evidence for or against restriction of genetic potency.

Comparative studies of chromosomes in three different tissues of an
insect larva (*Chironomus*) have been made [7]. These giant chromosomes taken from salivary gland cells, Malpighian tubule cells, and gut
epithelium show differences in number of longitudinal strands (degree of
polyteny) and in the structure of homologous bands. Interestingly
enough, the structure of a given band varies with different states of activity of the cell, being much enlarged, "puffed," in a chromosome from a
secreting salivary gland cell as compared with its size in a resting, non-
secreting cell. But change in chromosome structure may occur quite independently of genetic change. When amphibian oocytes and other
heavily yolked eggs are undergoing oogenesis, their chromosomes undergo
characteristic changes in shape and size, resulting in the so-called "lamp-
brush chromosomes." These changes are most marked at precisely the
time when the synthesis of yolk in the cytoplasm is at its peak. It has

therefore been suggested that the lamp-brush chromosomes play a role in the formation of the yolk reserves of the oocyte. Obviously, however, no permanent *genetic* change can occur during oogenesis. How can direct evidence be obtained for or against genetic changes associated with differentiation?

Nuclear Transplantation Studies

In 1938 Hans Spemann [60, p. 211] suggested an experiment which appeared to him at that time to be "somewhat fantastical," namely the introduction of nuclei from differentiated cells into enucleated eggs. "This experiment might possibly show," he predicted, "that even nuclei of differentiated cells can initiate normal development in the egg protoplasm." If so, Spemann argued, decisive information would thereby be provided as to whether every cell of the differentiated body contains the whole complement of hereditary determinants. We will find reason to question this argument later on, but first let us outline some of the ideas and experiments that formed the background for actual performance of Spemann's "fantastical" experiment some fifteen years after it was suggested. It is an interesting commentary on the evolution of concepts that quite independently several other biologists, apparently unaware of Spemann's suggestion, later pointed out the potential value of nuclear transplantation studies.

The idea of introducing a nucleus from a differentiated cell into an egg was a direct offshoot of Spemann's delayed nucleation experiments, in which, you will recall, an early descendant of the zygote nucleus crossed a protoplasmic bridge between two halves of a ligatured egg. He pointed out the technical difficulties involved if nuclei from later stages of development were to be used, first in isolating the donor nucleus, and second in introducing this nucleus into an egg devoid of a nucleus. "The first half of this experiment," Spemann says, ". . . might be attained by grinding the cells between two slides, whereas for the second, . . . I see no way for the moment." As it turned out, far gentler procedures had to be used to obtain undamaged donor nuclei, while enucleation and injection of nuclei had to wait upon development of precision instruments, one of which, the micromanipulator, was devised for problems entirely different from nuclear transplantation.

You may ask, why not approach the question directly by simply exchanging nuclei between fully differentiated adult cells in tissue culture? In this case, their cytoplasms being different, if their nuclei were identical, unchanged from the nucleus of the fertilized egg from which they arose, there should be no incompatibility. The transplanted nucleus should be capable of maintaining the life and specific character of its host cell. If the nuclei are different, however, such an exchange would not be a good test. One could not distinguish between nuclear as opposed to cytoplasmic differentiation. One must question also whether differentiated cytoplasm is a valid test object for the potencies of a transplanted nucleus? Might not the cytoplasm have undergone irreversible changes that render it unresponsive to even a totipotent nucleus? This latter objection cannot be made when the host cytoplasm consists of an enucleated egg.

Nuclear Transplantation in Unicellular Organisms

In actual fact, the first successful nuclear and cytoplasmic transplantations were made between unicellular organisms. An enucleated amoeba could be placed side by side with an intact amoeba and the nucleus of the latter pushed into the host with a blunt needle. When successfully performed, the transplantation is followed by division of the host cell and a clone of amoebae is obtained. If the original amoebae belong to different species, the character of the "hybrid" might be expected to indicate whether nucleus or cytoplasm has had the major influence in cellular differentiation. Unfortunately, in amoeba the differences are not very marked between species. Where it was possible to make a judgment, the hybrid often appeared to be intermediate in character.

More recent experiments have added the information that changes occur in both nucleus and cytoplasm when such a hybrid amoeba is made [23]. This follows from the results observed after back-transfer of nuclei from an established hybrid clone into their own original type of cytoplasm. For example, *Amoeba proteus* and *A. discoides* differ in three characteristics: (1) shape when moving, (2) average nuclear diameter, and (3) division rate, or frequency of division. When a *proteus* nucleus is transplanted into *discoides* cytoplasm to produce the hybrid P_nD_c, the latter is found to be intermediate between the two parent species in character 1, while more like the cytoplasmic parent in characters 2 and 3. The hybrid clone may survive for a month or even for years. After a number of generations, in the course of which the *proteus* chromosomes are replicating in *discoides* cytoplasm, the "proteus" nucleus is back-transferred to an enucleated *proteus* individual. The resulting amoebae have a division rate more like *discoides* than like *proteus*. After a long sojourn in *discoides* cytoplasm, the *proteus* nuclei have been modified to resemble *discoides* nuclei in some respects. On the other hand, when, after a number of generations, cytoplasm of an enucleated P_nD_c hybrid amoeba is renucleated with a *discoides* nucleus, the result is an amoeba which no longer shows the characters of the pure strain of *Amoeba discoides*. In a later chapter we will discuss similar experiments with amphibian hybrids and their implications for nuclear differentiation.

FIGURE 18. *Acetabularia mediterranea,* showing parasol-shaped caps at tops of thin stalks. (Brachet, 1962.)

In another set of classical experiments, interchanges were made between cytoplasms and nuclei of two species of the marine alga, *Acetabularia* [for references see 12]. This beautiful green plant consists of a single giant cell exhibiting considerable polarity and structural differentiation. Two to three centimeters in height, it possesses a rootlike base (rhizoid) in which the nucleus is found, a stalk, and an enlarged cap, which in *A. mediterranea* is shaped somewhat like a flat parasol (Fig. 18). The cap of *A. crenulata,* deeply notched and scalloped, is entirely different in appearance from the other species.

A stem of *A. mediterranea* is cut off just at the base, its nucleus left behind in the base. The cap is removed and the cut stem then is grafted to a base of *A. crenulata,* which, of course, retains the *crenulata* nucleus. The reciprocal transplant is made as diagrammed in Fig. 19. In both instances, a new cap is formed from the distal end of the stalk. While the first cap formed is sometimes intermediate in character, subsequent decapitations result in regenerated caps more nearly of the pure nuclear type. In both instances, eventually the new cap has the character of the species of the nucleus above which the stalk was grafted and not that of the intervening cytoplasmic stalk. Nuclear products presumably reach the regenerating cap by moving through the stalk. In fact, a cap with

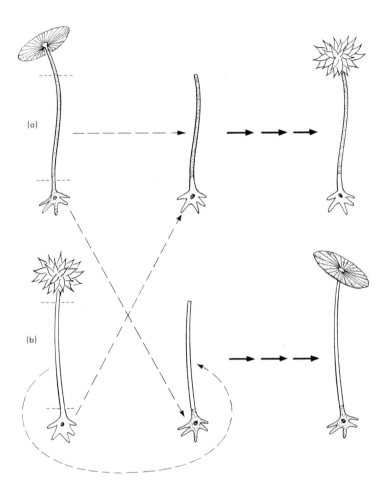

FIGURE 19. Transplantation experiments using two species of *Acetabularia* which differ in shape of the "cap," the structure which produces gametes for the next generation of this alga. The character of the cap is finally determined by the species quality of the nucleus provided in the chimera. Arrows in sequence indicate several successive decapitations. The *A. mediterranea* material is shaded to facilitate tracing it through the grafting experiments. In (a) stalk from *A. mediterranea* is grafted to base from *A. crenulata*. In (b) the reciprocal graft is diagrammed. (After Hämmerling in Srb and Owen, 1949.)

characteristics of the nuclear species will be regenerated in an *enucleate* *Acetabularia* if only the cap and not the adjacent stalk is cut off.

Additional evidence for the production by the nucleus of species-specific "morphogenetic substances" comes from ingenious grafts between two or three rhizoidal pieces. Intermediate type caps are formed from binucleate grafts containing one *A. mediterranea* and one *A. crenulata* nucleus. When a composite is made containing two *crenulata* and one *mediterranea* nuclei, the successive regenerating caps eventually more closely resemble *crenulata*. Regeneration of a cap involves protein synthesis, and from the grafting experiments, it is concluded that the specific proteins synthesized are determined *ultimately* by the DNA-containing structural genes. We emphasize *ultimately* because the stalk has been found to contain no measurable trace of DNA, yet stalks (lacking nuclei) can regenerate a species-specific cap for a time.

It has been found that removal of the nucleus stimulates RNA synthesis, although normally the nucleus is more active than the cytoplasm in forming RNA. Furthermore, experiments have shown that the presence of the nucleus is not necessary for short-term protein synthesis, although it is required for *prolonged* protein synthesis. It seems reasonable to assume that the species specificity of regenerated caps is most closely associated with cytoplasmic RNA formed originally according to a molecular pattern determined by the nucleus.

Note also that in these experiments we fall far short of the ideal objective of transplanting a nucleus alone. Relatively large amounts of cytoplasm also are being transplanted along with the rhizoidal nucleus. Can we say with any degree of certainty that this cytoplasm is totally lacking in molecular structures capable of directing specific protein syntheses? The answer as indicated above is no—and we shall talk about this further in our final chapter.

The experiments with amoeba and *Acetabularia* formed part of the background for the courageous work of Briggs and King during the 1950's. For it was these workers who patiently and skillfully worked out the methods necessary to perform Spemann's "fantastical experiment." Their results with the frog egg have stimulated other investigators to pursue the problem of nuclear differentiation in other organisms and other test systems. Because the work of Briggs and King already is recognized as classical, and because it so frequently is quoted without thorough comprehension of all the factors involved, we shall present their methods and results in detail. This work affords an outstanding illustration of excellence in care and attention to sources of error in performance of an experiment, and of admirable caution in interpretation of results [18].

NUCLEAR TRANSPLANTATION IN VERTEBRATE EMBRYOS

Control Experiments

1. What can egg cytoplasm minus a nucleus do? We already have explained the choice by Briggs and King of egg cytoplasm as the test object for the potencies of transplanted nuclei. The enucleated ovum is relatively undifferentiated, with the reservations mentioned in connection with specialization of ooplasms during maturation in the ovary. Such an enucleated egg undergoes cleavage and partial blastula formation, but never reaches even the beginnings of gastrulation. The non-nucleated cells of such arrested blastulae cannot respond even to normal inductors. This is shown by grafting groups of "achromosomal" cells from arrested partial blastulae into host eggs at gastrula or neurula stages. Grafts into the future head region (animal pole region) of a young gastrula, as well as grafts into flank regions of young neurulae where they are exposed to a variety of mesodermal inductors, fuse with adjacent host ectoderm and heal well. Within a matter of hours, or four days at most, however, the graft cells round up and the graft is lost.

The enucleate egg cytoplasm alone therefore is shown to be incapable of differentiation. Supplied with its own "undifferentiated" zygote nucleus, the egg cytoplasm forms a normal embryo. What will this egg cytoplasm do when supplied with a nucleus from a differentiated cell?

2. How can the success of enucleation of the egg be proved? It was necessary to develop a completely dependable method for removing the egg nucleus, since proof of enucleation cannot be obtained on the egg actually used as host for a transplanted nucleus until the experiment has been terminated and the embryo killed and studied histologically. Briggs and King modified the method previously worked out by Porter [53] for producing androgenetic haploids and achieved more than 99% success at enucleation of the egg. How could they prove this?

When the egg is pricked with a *clean* glass needle, it rotates within 10 to 15 minutes and the egg nucleus appears as a small black dot in a somewhat depigmented spot near the surface at the animal pole. If the egg nucleus is allowed to remain, five to ten hours later abnormal and abortive cleavage furrows are seen. If the egg nucleus is removed after activation by inserting a glass needle beneath the nucleus and moving the needle upward, no cleavage furrows are seen five to ten hours later. At fifteen hours, such eggs may show some few abortive cleavage furrows.

Another test for success of the enucleation procedure can be made by fertilizing with normal sperm and removing the egg nucleus immediately. The resulting haploid eggs give rise to tadpoles with the "haploid syndrome" of gross visible defects and the haploid number of chromosomes that can be counted in tail tip squashes.

3. How can damage to the test nucleus be minimized? This potential source of error proved one of the most troublesome, and presents an excellent example of the manner in which the living organism tends to thwart the most carefully conceived of "ideal" experiments. First of all, a "dry" nucleus cannot be handled; it must be picked up and injected into the enucleate egg in some liquid medium. We do not, of course, have a formula for the chemical composition of the normal nuclear medium. Secondly, whereas the object of the transplantation experiments was to test the potencies of nuclear materials *alone,* a nucleus entirely free of all traces of cytoplasm is impossible to obtain—and even were it feasible, such a naked nucleus might well succumb to injurious effects of the abnormal injection medium. Each transplanted nucleus therefore carries with it traces of cytoplasm estimated to be of the order of magnitude of approximately 1/100,000 the volume of the egg cytoplasm into which the test nucleus is injected. Since the contaminating cytoplasm is of perinuclear location, its importance might exceed what mere volume ratios tend to minimize.

The meticulous thoroughness characteristic of the work of Briggs and King is illustrated by the exhaustive preliminary tests they made with various kinds of media for injection of nuclei. Four kinds of "simple" inorganic salt mixtures (all modifications of Ringer's original solution) were tested, in addition to media containing adult frog body cavity fluid, nutrients, blood serum, or homogenates from frog eggs or embryos. As it turned out, none of these modified media gave better results than the one they had used initially, the salt mixture devised by Niu and Twitty for culture of amphibian neural crest cells. Even these preparatory tests required time and as much skill as the final experiments.

We have presented these sources of error at some length for several reasons. The reliability of conclusions drawn from any set of experiments in biology depends upon the care with which the actual experimental manipulations were executed and the experimenter's comprehension of variables that intrude beyond the one variable he is attempting to test. A reliable investigator presents this side of the story to his readers. He also describes as precisely as possible how the experiments were made so that his colleagues can both judge the validity of the conclusions drawn and be able to repeat and extend the work described. The publications of Briggs and King meet these criteria of excellence, and their methods have been used profitably in other laboratories where investigators have heeded their warning that ". . . results of this order of magnitude . . . cannot be obtained by a beginner. The technique requires a lot of practice and constant attention to detail to be successful."

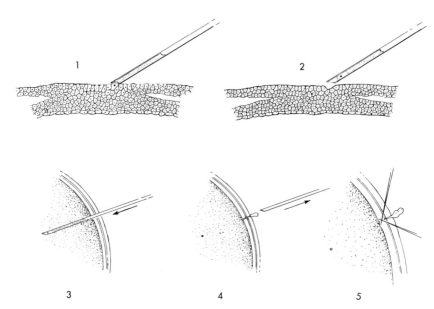

FIGURE 20. Method devised by Briggs and King for transplanting a nucleus into an enucleated ovum. In this instance the nucleus is taken from a blastula cell. 1. Blastula cell being drawn up into tip of a fine glass pipette. 2. Cell surface broken as cell enters pipette. 3. Ejection of nucleus into an already prepared enucleate ovum. 4. Small exovate of egg cytoplasm resulting from withdrawal of the micropipette. 5. Neck of exovate clipped off by a pair of microneedles. (Briggs and King, 1953.)

The Method

The following account is quoted from the original report of Briggs and King concerning transplantation of blastula cell nuclei into enucleated eggs (Fig. 20).

"First, the outer jelly coats are removed from the enucleated eggs, and they are placed in hemispherical depressions along the periphery of a wax bottomed watch glass containing Niu and Twitty solution . . . The donor blastula, collapsed as a result of removing the egg membranes, is now placed in the center of the operating dish with the flattened animal hemisphere uppermost. With glass needles a small defect is made near the center of the animal hemisphere and one of the sub-surface cells is removed and placed on the surface coat of the adjacent intact portion of the blastula. This surface serves admirably as an operation platform. It is soft, and yet the isolated cell has no tendency to stick to it, so that subsequent manipulations can be carried out without inadvertently damaging the cell. The cell is first drawn up into a *clean* micropipette with an inner diameter slightly smaller than that of the cell. The relative size of cell and pipette is very important, and the manipulation requires considerable practice. If the cytoplasm is dispersed as the cell is drawn up into the pipette, the nucleus will be damaged or killed and there will be no genuine cleavage of the recipient egg. On the other hand, if the cell surface remains intact, the nucleus subsequently will remain isolated from the egg cytoplasm and again there will be no cleavage. In other words, in order to obtain a successful nuclear transfer it is necessary to break the cell surface without dispersing its contents. . . . With the cell in this condition near the tip of the pipette, the pipette is pushed well into an enucleated egg, and the fluid column is moved down just enough to eject the broken cell, thus liberating the nucleus into the egg cytoplasm. . . . As the pipette is slowly withdrawn it pulls the surface coat of the egg up against the vitelline membrane, forming a small canal through which an exovate starts to form. This canal is cut immediately with glass needles. . . . Finally the egg is removed from the operating dish and placed in a small Stender dish in spring water.

"All of the manipulations described above [for enucleation] are done free-hand under the dissecting microscope . . . [at a] magnification of about 60 diameters. . . .

"The second part of the operation, the transplantation of the blastula cell nucleus into the enucleated egg, is done under a magnification of about 90 diameters with a dissecting microscope fitted with a foot-focussing attachment. The construction of the micropipettes used in the transfer is quite important. . . ."

Evidence for the dependability of the enucleation procedure already has been presented. Further evidence comes from the fact that when later sectioned the experimental eggs are found to contain the egg nucleus in the exovate.

The Transplantability of Blastula and Gastrula Nuclei

A most remarkable fact, first of all, is that even in the earliest experiments reported, more than half the recipient eggs cleaved, and the majority of the cleaved eggs developed into complete embryos. These embryos then consist of cells containing nuclei derived from the transplanted blastula nucleus. A comparison of results of transplantation of blastula and gastrula nuclei both taken from subsurface cells in the region of the animal pole is presented in Table 2.

Thus early gastrula nuclei from cells in the blastocoele roof still may participate in all the types of differentiation necessary to produce a complete embryo. Early gastrula ectoderm cells of course are totipotent at this stage, in the sense of being able to form a wide variety of tissues depending upon the inductors to which they are exposed. But what about

TABLE 2

Source of donor nucleus	Total eggs injected	Normal cleavage		Complete embryos	
		Actual number	%	Actual number	%
Blastula	204	116	57	69	34
Early gastrula	135	52	38	20	15

nuclei from cells which already have been determined to follow a specific pathway of differentiation?

Such "determined" cells first can be obtained at late gastrula stage, by which time the presumptive notochord (chorda-mesoderm) region will form only mesodermal structures in transplants or explants. At the same stage the presumptive neural plate region is determined with respect to ability to form eye structures. First attempts to transfer nuclei from these "determined" cells were disappointing in that only a very small proportion of the recipient eggs even cleaved. Again a recess from the central problem had to be declared while Briggs and King analyzed the reasons for decreasing success in nuclear transplantation with increasing age of donor embryo.

At this point the entire program might have suffered a premature demise, or at least a severe setback. If nuclei of partially differentiated cells already have undergone some change that deprives them of ability to engage in the cleavage cycle of the egg, then it would be impossible to test such nuclei for possible qualitative changes in their ability to control cytoplasmic differentiation. Since a low but definite percent of late gastrula nuclei *could* initiate cleavage, it occurred to Briggs and King that nuclei were transplantable only at a particular mitotic phase, and that frequency of this phase decreased with stage of development to account for the decreasing frequency of successful transfers from blastula, early gastrula, to late gastrula. For example, it might be supposed that only interphase nuclei with nuclear membrane intact are transplantable and that the proportion of nuclei at interphase is lower at gastrula than at blastula stages.

Frequencies of the various mitotic phases observed in animal hemisphere cells of blastulae and early gastrulae were tabulated. There was no clearcut relationship between transplantability and mitotic phase of a nucleus. While transplantability decreased from 34% to 15% between blastula and early gastrula stages, the proportion of nuclei in the interphase is slightly higher at the later stage (92% compared with 89%).

It appeared more probable then that nuclei of older embryos might be more susceptible to damage during transplantation. And this was a possibility about which something could be done. Mechanical or chemical damage to the nucleus during manipulation did appear probable when it was determined by direct measurement of volume of cytoplasm that the readily transplantable blastula cell nuclei were protected by more than twice the volume of cytoplasm that surrounds the smaller gastrula cells. Furthermore, cells and cell layers of older embryos stick together more firmly and are more liable to be damaged during the struggle to isolate them in preparation for obtaining the donor nuclei.

It was a relatively simple matter to confirm this suspicion. Eggs which failed to cleave after injection of a nucleus were sectioned and stained with the Feulgen reagent for chromatin. Their chromosomes were indeed badly damaged—condensed, vacuolated, or even fragmented. Conversely, eggs that had cleaved normally after injection contained normal nuclei as judged by the distribution and shape of the chromosomes in stained sections.

More months of hard work on technical detail then had to follow. It was at this time that the eight different media mentioned earlier were compared for their ability to protect a nucleus from damage during transplantation. Unfortunately an unbroken injected cell would not initiate cleavage because the nucleus was isolated by the cell membrane from contact with the host egg cytoplasm. Even the simplest inorganic medium tested contains seven different salts, the concentration of each of which could be varied in an attempt at improved results. The original medium gave the best results. The nucleus proved to be highly sensitive to changes in the medium.

A more successful modification of the method involved a gentler procedure for isolating donor cells from the later embryos, where increased adhesiveness between cells presents a problem. This was achieved by placing the embryo in a calcium-free trypsin solution to facilitate softening of the intercellular "cementing" materials so that the desired embryonic layer could be readily peeled away. Separation of the layer into component individual cells was aided by passing it through a versene solution (ethylene diamine tetraacetic acid, more commonly known as EDTA). In the case of early gastrula stages, these chemical aids to dissociation improved several fold both percent cleavage and later development as compared with the transplantability of nuclei from cells isolated merely by dissection with glass needles.

Now, finally, it was possible to return to the question of nuclear differentiation during later stages. When donor nuclei were taken from cells in the chorda-mesoderm of *late* gastrula stages, the improved methods more than doubled the proportion of host eggs that cleaved to form complete blastulae. There was, however, no improvement in the later development of these blastulae, the majority of which still stopped

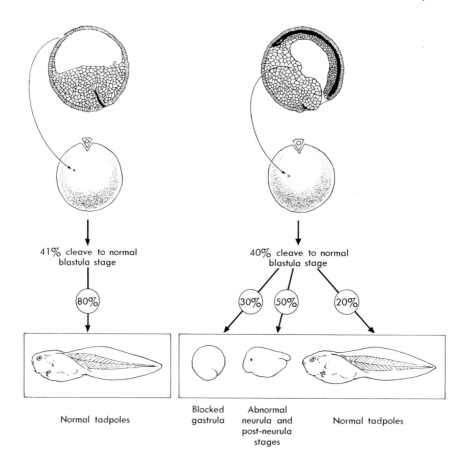

41% cleave to normal
blastula stage

(80%)

Normal tadpoles

40% cleave to normal
blastula stage

(30%) (50%)   (20%)

Blocked   Abnormal
gastrula   neurula and
           post-neurula
           stages

Normal tadpoles

FIGURE 21. Comparison of ability to support development of transplanted early gastrula ectoderm nuclei (left) with late gastrula endoderm nuclei (right). (Data from King and Briggs, 1955).

development at blastula, gastrula, or abnormal prehatching stages. An intrinsic change in some of these nuclei from a "determined" area of the late gastrula was thus indicated—the first breakthrough in this difficult work. This change at first appeared to have a degree of specificity in the sense that the transplanted chorda-mesoderm nuclei gave rise to embryos deficient in central nervous system structures, although possessing a normal appearing notochord and somites.

When endoderm nuclei of late gastrula stage were transplanted, 40% of the recipient eggs formed normal blastulae as did controls that received "undifferentiated" nuclei from animal hemisphere cells of early gastrulae. Further development, however, was quite different in the two sets. Whereas the "early gastrula" embryos that reached the blastula stage gave rise to more than 80% normal tadpoles, the "endoderm blastulae" were usually arrested in blastula, gastrula, or abnormal pre-hatching stages. In the experiment diagrammed in Fig. 21, for example, of the host eggs that reached the blastula stage, 30% blocked at gastrula; 50% formed embryos with ectodermal deficiencies, small central nervous systems, reduced sense organs, and irregularly thickened ectoderm; and only 20% formed normal tadpoles.

This range of variation in degree and quality of development taken at face value suggests that most endoderm nuclei have suffered some "genetic" restriction by late gastrula stage. If so, this nuclear differentiation appears to proceed in a gradual manner in any given region of the developing embryo, not synchronously in all cells at once.

NUCLEAR CLONING AND ITS SIGNIFICANCE

When considered critically, however, these first results with endoderm nuclei still were open to criticism on the basis of simple injury to nuclei during the manipulations, such that although the nuclei were capable of supporting cleavage, more subtle damages prevented normal differentiation. For this reason in part and also because they wished to test the stability and permanence of the presumed nuclear changes, Briggs and King undertook the laborious task of preparing clones of nuclei. A nuclear clone consists of a group of nuclei all derived from a single endoderm nucleus. Such data are not easily obtained. In order to establish 27 nuclear clones, a total of approximately 850 nuclear transfers had to be made. Nine of the 27 nuclear clones were control clones involving serial transfers of undifferentiated blastula nuclei.

The results of one set of serial transplantations of donor endoderm nuclei taken from the presumptive anterior midgut region of the late gastrula are shown in Fig. 22. The essence of the results may be summarized by the following statements. (1) The original recipients of late gastrula endoderm nuclei gave a range of different kinds of development from arrested gastrulae to normal embryos. (2) When one blastula from the original recipient generation was sacrificed to provide nuclei for transfer to a new group of enucleated eggs, the latter displayed a quite uniform type of development in both first, second, and subsequent generations. "This is in contrast to the wide variety of developmental types seen among the original recipients of the different endoderm nuclei." This is also in contrast to the results of serial transplantation experiments with nuclei of undifferentiated blastula cells. In the majority of experiments, these control nuclei gave rise to clones of normal embryos.

To summarize then, nuclear cloning proved that some of the endoderm nuclei had undergone a stable, reproducible change expressed under the

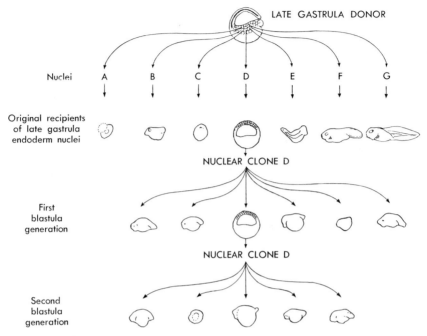

FIGURE 22. Serial transplantation of endoderm cell nuclei taken from the presumptive anterior midgut region of the late gastrula of *Rana pipiens*. Transferred to enucleated eggs, these endoderm cell nuclei promote a variety of types of development, as shown for the "original recipients" in the diagram. However, one of the original recipients, sacrificed in the blastula stage, provides nuclei for a single clone which shows more uniform development in the "second blastula generation." Thus some nuclei of the late gastrula have undergone a certain amount of differentiation as revealed by this kind of test. (King and Briggs, 1956.)

conditions of the experiment in their incapacity to support normal development of an enucleated ovum.

How specific are these nuclear changes? Let us turn back now to the results of the experiments diagrammed in Fig. 21. Of the 40% of the host eggs that gave rise to normal blastula stages, half (50%) of these blastulae developed into abnormal neurula and post-neurula stages. Upon closer observation these neurulae could be classified as (1) 40% which exhibited deficiencies in ectodermal and mesodermal structures together with more normal differentiation of the endoderm; (2) 10% which developed with deficiencies in any or all of the three germ layers. These data suggest that some of the late gastrula endoderm cell nuclei have become restricted in their ability to participate fully in differentiation of mesodermal and ectodermal structures. The exceptions, those nuclei which did not conform to an endodermal pattern, had to be explained.

In a careful investigation [19a] the nonconforming group was found to have abnormal chromosome complements. Fragmented chromosomes, ring chromosomes, and aneuploidy characterized the descendant nuclei of the transplanted endoderm cell nuclei in this class. A similar picture of abnormal chromosome content was observed in the 30% of host embryos which blocked at early gastrula (Fig. 21). These embryos therefore are not valid test objects for the question of nuclear differentiation because aneuploidy leads to abnormal development quite aside from possible changes in the genetic character or function of a nucleus.

Valid cases constitute those nuclei in which the chromosome complement remains euploid following nuclear transfer. Such embryos follow either of two pathways of differentiation: (1) They develop normally to give the 20% normal tadpoles indicated in Fig. 21; or (2) they reach neurula stages with abnormalities in ectodermal and mesodermal derivatives, but their endodermal structures are normal.

These results strengthen the case for a characteristic nuclear differentiation in endoderm cells. Whether other cell types exhibit similar specificity in their nuclear differentiation can be determined only by the same kind of careful investigations with nuclei from presumptive epidermis, presumptive neural plate and the various regions of presumptive mesodermal structures.

The cause of the chromosomal abnormalities is under investigation. Simple damage due to the transplantation technique is unlikely as an explanation. One aspect of nuclear differentiation may be the acquisition of specific requirements for normal chromosome replication [19a]. If this be the case, descendants of a transplanted late gastrula endoderm cell nucleus may be unable to replicate and to function normally in cytoplasm deficient in the specific precursors required as a result of such nuclear differentiation.

NUCLEAR DIFFERENTIATION AND GERM CELLS: A RECURRENT PROBLEM

Let us turn back once more to the question of totipotency of germ cell nuclei. When the experiments of Briggs and King first became widely known, many biologists tended to read into the fact of nuclear differentiation the further implication that germ cells must remain or become totipotent during development. The fact that somatic cell nuclei under certain circumstances become restricted in their ability to participate in differentiation tells us nothing about their genetic totipotency.

On the other hand, there is some evidence in favor of the ability of endoderm nuclei from cells *outside* the presumptive germ cell region to enter into the germ line. Somatic cell nuclei, which still retain the ability to promote normal development, also retain the ability to support germ-cell formation, i.e., ovaries with growing oocytes [19]. Endoderm nuclei from hatched *Xenopus* tadpoles have been reported by Gurdon [36] to give rise to sexually mature adults. It may be mentioned here that evidently the restriction of nuclear function in somatic cells of *Xenopus* occurs at a later stage of development than in the frog embryo. Minor differences in the techniques used in the two instances might, however, be important contributing factors. For example, finding it technically impossible in *Xenopus* to enucleate the recipient egg by means of glass needles, Fischberg and his co-workers used a micro-beam of ultraviolet light to eliminate the egg chromosomes from participating in development. The achromatic portions of the nucleus, as well as the components of the UV-injured chromosomes, thus are present, and might conceivably alter the properties of the introduced test nucleus.

We have come to the end of a long story told in some detail, because the nuclear transplantation work provides an excellent example of the manner in which even the most skillful and critical workers are to some extent frustrated in performance of "the ideal experiment" by the very characteristics of the organism which they attempt to understand. This classic work is, of course, not the end but the beginning for future work. Still unresolved is the question whether such changes in nuclei play a *constructive* role in normal development. A nucleus may have lost the ability to interact with egg cytoplasm to bring about normal development, but that is not the normal job of an endoderm nucleus from late gastrula or tadpole. The nuclear changes revealed in these experiments do not necessarily imply changes in the basic molecular content and potential properties of the structural genes. Loss of gene *function* could conceivably come about through the influence of other nuclear components, which in turn might be modified by cytoplasmic differences among the various regions of the egg.

As to the first point, the "ideal" test for a nucleus from a cell at an advanced stage of differentiation would be to examine its ability to support development of an enucleated egg only after this test nucleus had been serially transplanted into successively younger cytoplasms of earlier stages of development. In other words: Run the "film" backward, instead of throwing a "differentiating" nucleus back immediately into the relatively undifferentiated cytoplasm of the activated ovum. Such an experiment appears as "fantastical" in terms of feasibility as was Spemann's suggestion, in 1938, of nuclear transplantation. It is possible, however, that experiments to answer this question can be devised in terms of contemporary concepts of gene action to be discussed in the last chapter. With respect to the influence of other nuclear components upon gene function we must await further progress in molecular genetics.

8

Hybrid Embryos and Development

Another approach to the problem of the roles of nucleus and cytoplasm in developmental events is provided by introducing the nucleus of one species into the egg cytoplasm of another species. Many workers in many countries have made such studies, and we must select purely on the basis of familiarity some examples drawn from some interspecific crosses between frogs of North America.

The information to be gained from such experiments depends upon several factors, of which we may mention two. The hybrid embryo must live long enough that the differential characteristics between the two species are apparent. Secondly, reciprocal crosses should be made. The chromosome complements of a diploid hybrid reciprocal cross are identical. If reciprocal crosses give different developmental results, cytoplasmic factors mediated through the ovum would be implicated.

EFFECTS OF A FOREIGN NUCLEUS ON EARLY DEVELOPMENT

A few years ago, Moore [48] tabulated the results of 140 diploid hybrid crosses between various species of frogs and toads. Over 90% of these hybrids gave some development, and of these, 42% formed normal tadpoles or even reached the adult stage. If we have as our foremost question just when the nucleus exerts its first effects on the quality or specific character of development, we are most interested in hybrids that block at some early stage. On the other hand, if the block occurs too early, we may not be able to distinguish characteristic species differences.

One ingenious method for overcoming this difficulty is to graft some region of the hybrid embryo into a normal host and follow its differentiation. This procedure, however, introduces a new source of error in that the normal host may produce substances or conditions that affect the quality of differentiation of the grafted hybrid tissues. A more valid approach is to find some characteristic interspecific difference that becomes manifest very early in development. Such a character is developmental rate at different temperatures in various species. For example, the rate of development at 18°C is higher in *Rana sylvatica* than in

Rana pipiens. What will be the comparative rates of development at 18°C of the reciprocal diploid hybrid crosses?

In general, Moore found that in those diploid hybrids which blocked at early gastrula stage the rate of development corresponded to that of the maternal parent species. The cytoplasm rather than the nucleus had the predominant influence up to gastrulation. In those hybrids in which development continued beyond the gastrula stage, the rate at first, during cleavage and gastrulation, approximated that of the maternal species but was altered in the paternal direction at neurula stages and later.

Reciprocal crosses gave interesting morphological differences, the significance of which was that clearly sooner or later the cytoplasm affected the expression of the genetic potencies of the nuclei. For the sake of illustration, let us look at the diploid hybrids made by crossing northern and southern individuals of the common American leopard frog, *Rana pipiens* [28]. When eggs of northern individuals are fertilized with sperm of southern individuals (northern-egg hybrids), abnormal, defective embryos with enlarged head structures (brain, notochord, mouth, and suckers) develop. The reciprocal cross (southern-egg hybrids) produces embryos with small heads, and reduced or even complete absence of eyes, olfactory organs, and mouth.

These curious facts fall into some sort of pattern when one learns that at a given relatively low temperature (16°C) northern leopard frogs exhibit a more rapid rate of development than do southern individuals. Development of head structures represents a complex series of embryonic inductions, in each of which two principal factors are involved: competence of reacting tissue, and state or quantity of the inductor tissue. If the sperm nucleus is playing a role at these stages, as is probable (cytoplasmic effects being preponderant only until the beginning of gastrulation) then one might hypothesize that with southern chromosomes, duration of competence of the ectoderm to respond to the various inductors is longer.

While this possibility has not yet been explored in the case of the north-south hybrids, we do know that in a European frog (*Rana esculenta*) if embryos are raised at 12°C, the lens of the eye will form from appropriate head ectoderm even in the absence of the optic cup which normally serves as its inductor. At 12°C then, the lens exhibits self-differentiation. When embryos are raised at 25°C, no lenses will form without optic cups, an example of embryonic induction [64]. The degree of competence to respond to inductors thus can be a function of temperature.

An alternative hypothesis has been proposed [28] for the north-south hybrids, and some evidence has been mustered to support it. "Northern-egg hybrids had an excessive number of cells in notochord and central nervous system. . . . Southern-egg hybrids had a deficiency of notochord and neural cells." It was therefore suggested that "some situation in the cytoplasm (which may be coupled with adaptation to cooler temperatures) results in a change in the presumptive value of blastula tissue so that more cells become notochord than normally would do so. . . ." Crucial experiments that would permit a choice between the above alternative explanations are as yet lacking.

This excursion has taken us into the problem of embryonic induction, which we cannot properly treat in so brief a book. Let us return to our main line of investigation and ask what other problems of nucleo-cytoplasmic interaction are illuminated by studies with hybrid embryos.

THE PROBLEM OF ARRESTED GASTRULAE

Among the more interesting hybrids are those which block at the beginning of gastrulation. The length of time during which these "arrested gastrulae" survive after onset of the block varies from one hybrid to another, as shown for the three crosses diagrammed in Fig. 23. The block to gastrulation thus has different characteristics from one cross to another. A second type of difference appears when the rate of respiration (or oxygen consumption) is compared in two different hybrid arrested gastrulae [4]. In the cross *pipiens* female × *sylvatica* male, oxygen consumption rises slowly until the beginning of gastrulation. At this time, development ceases, although the egg lives on for four or five days at 15 to 18°C without showing any signs of cytolysis. Oxygen consumption does not rise further in the arrested hybrid gastrulae, while the control normal *pipiens* embryos continue to show an increase in respiratory rate. However, in another hybrid cross (*pipiens* female × *clamitans* male) in which development ceases at early gastrula stage, the rate of respiration continues to increase just as in control *pipiens* embryos.

Now, of course, oxygen consumption itself is a rather unspecific characteristic of biological processes. The specificity comes from control of the transfer of energy obtained from oxidation to molecules that perform some specific task—whether it be muscle contraction, secretion of substances against a concentration gradient, or the synthesis of new proteins in a differentiating nerve cell, for example. Any of several links in the energy supply-utilization chain could be broken in the hybrid embryos. A substrate is oxidized by a long series of individual enzyme-catalyzed reactions, any one or more of which could be defective in a given hybrid embryo. If the energy *supply* became crucial at gastrulation, then blocked respiration and blocked development would follow. It is, however, also conceivable that nothing is wrong with the energy-*yielding* reactions, but that the energy does not get transferred so as to maintain

COMPOSITION OF HYBRID	STAGE OF BLOCK	STAGE OF CONTROLS WHEN BLOCKED HYBRIDS DIE

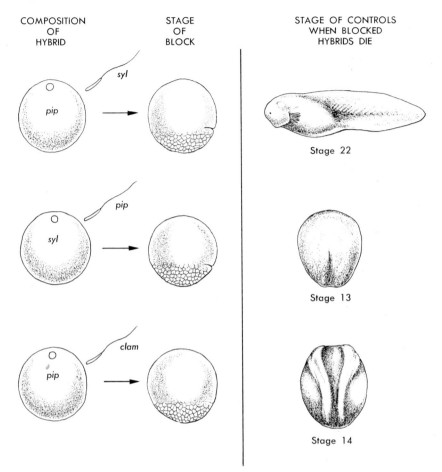

FIGURE 23. Comparison of three interspecies hybrids, all of which cease development at the early gastrula stage. The fact that the basic cause of this hybrid block must differ among the three crosses is suggested by the variation in length of time they survive before cytolysis begins. This is shown at the right by means of the diagrams of stage of development of control embryos at the time when death of hybrids occurs. *Rana pipiens* is abbreviated as *pip*; *R. sylvatica*, as *syl*; and *R. clamitans*, as *clam*. The dorsal lip of the gastrula in the *clamitans* hybrid appears as a faint pigment line that lasts only for an hour or two. Relative sizes of gametes and embryos are not represented in the diagram.

the necessary stores of energy-rich compounds of which adenosine triphosphate (ATP) is an example. Finally, the defective link in the energy supply-demand chain could occur if the energy is not accepted for lack of some needed enzyme or substrate. If a given hybrid fails at either of the two latter steps, it may cease developing, even though its respiration continues to rise at a normal rate. Thus different types of interspecies hybrids need not be expected to show a simple correlation between block to development and block to respiration. And they do not.

The above possibilities all assume that development blocks because of some prior block in energy supply or transfer. Is it not possible that respiration blocks *following* cessation of development? This possibility has been suggested [33], namely that respiration is blocked because the embryo is not developing, although, of course, it would apply only to those hybrids where developmental and respiratory arrest coincide and not to those in which respiration continues to rise at the normal rate. If ATP is not dephosphorylated to supply energy-rich phosphate to some acceptor(s), the respiration required to maintain the normal supply of ATP from the reaction $ADP \rightleftharpoons ATP$ will be lowered. Which is cause and which effect is not yet known with certainty, and the situation may well differ among the various kinds of arrested hybrid gastrulae.

It is of interest, however, that the blocked gastrulae of the *pipiens* female × *sylvatica* male have been shown to possess the respiratory "machinery" to support a perfectly normal respiratory rate, even though they fail to use it. This was demonstrated by making homogenates and comparing their respiration with that of normal *pipiens* homogenates. The two kinds of homogenates gave comparable rates of oxygen consumption [33]. Is this particular hybrid block, then, caused by failure of some intracellular changes in the molecular or ultrastructural components responsible for enzyme-substrate unions? We look forward to further studies on this question.

Another facet of the work with hybrid embryos concerns their nucleic acid metabolism [12]. Here surely we might expect to be closer to the heart of the question of what first goes wrong when a foreign sperm is introduced into egg cytoplasm. Deoxyribonucleic acid (DNA), closely related to the "structural" gene, has been measured in normal and hybrid embryos. In the *pipiens* female × *sylvatica* male, hybrid DNA rises normally and continues to rise for some time after the stage of developmental arrest. Although we must look for other methods of determining whether the hybrid's DNA is *qualitatively* the same as that of normal eggs, quantitatively at least the block to development cannot be attributed to DNA starvation.

With ribonucleic acid, however, the story is different, for the hybrids show distinct abnormalities in their RNA content and distribution. Many of the nuclei in the arrested gastrulae are found to contain abnormally large nucleoli, more than the normal number of nucleoli, and an overload of RNA. And yet no increase in *cytoplasmic* RNA can be detected in the blocked hybrid egg. It is as though the hybrid nuclei synthesize too much of the "wrong" kind of RNA, which cannot be used by the cytoplasm to assist in protein synthesis.

There is some evidence for this hypothesis from the fact that when a piece of tissue from a blocked hybrid gastrula is transplanted into a normal host, the hybrid nuclei become more normal and the hybrid cytoplasm begins to synthesize RNA. It is not known as yet by what means the healthy normal tissues accomplish this therapy to the transplant, but diffusible products may be involved.

In the several aspects that have been studied, the hybrid embryo's abnormalities appear to be quite general, involving the entire egg. In the case of the lower respiration of blocked hybrid embryos, all parts of the gastrula have a lower rate of oxygen consumption [62]. Furthermore, both the competence of the ectoderm to respond to an inductor and the inducing ability of the presumptive chorda-mesoderm are lower in the hybrid. When presumptive chorda-mesoderm is grafted into the blastocoele of a normal host, the "organizer" region will induce a fair secondary embryo. Presumptive ectoderm of a hybrid embryo grafted above chorda-mesoderm is competent to respond by forming a nervous system, although the quality of the latter is somewhat subnormal [48].

Such "revitalization" phenomena of hybrid tissues put into a healthy, normal host environment show that the hybrid tissue, taken in time, is capable of exhibiting fairly normal differentiation potencies. In our own laboratory we have obtained additional indications that this is true. We culture very small groups of cells from the dorsal and presumptive lateral lips of the blocked *pipiens* × *sylvatica* gastrula. Left in place, these cells would never differentiate and would cytolyze along with the rest of the intact blocked gastrula. Removed and cultured *in vitro*, however, the cells form several kinds of nerve cells and fibers, pigment cells, mesenchyme, and heart (cardiac) muscle cells that exhibit rhythmic pulsation.

Altogether the various types of hybrid embryos provide a challenging body of material for future investigations using contemporary techniques of investigation. We shall return to one such new approach in a later section when we take up serial transplantation of nuclei between two species.

9

Nucleocytoplasmic Interactions in Hybrid Embryos

In the course of the preceding chapters we have had occasion to mention a number of experimentally produced abnormal combinations of nucleus and cytoplasm. It is worthwhile at this point to pause and put together in tabular form a few examples of such "chromosome juggling" in order to formulate some specific questions for further experiment and discussion. Table 3 is an adaptation and abbreviation of a chart presented in a paper by Moore [48].

Let us ask a few questions based upon the data in Table 3 and suggest a few answers which need experimental confirmation. First of all, why don't haploids develop normally? As we have already mentioned, none of the several hypotheses thus far advanced have found conclusive experimental support. From the table it is apparent that whether the single set of chromosomes of the haploid is of maternal or paternal derivation makes no difference in the poor development observed. The hypothesis that in haploids, lethal genes are present which are not balanced by normal alleles is negated by item 1 of the table. To say that the abnormally low nucleocytoplasmic ratio results in poor utilization of yolk reserves poses more questions than the statement answers. Yolk utilization in the amphibian egg goes on at a slow pace which is facilitated in part at least by the enzyme phosphoprotein phosphatase. The activity of this enzyme depends, of course, upon pH. But there is also evidence that the concentration of ATP regulates the rate at which phosphate is liberated from the phosphoprotein of yolk for use in synthesizing nucleic acids and other constituents of the differentiating egg cytoplasm [4]. It is indeed conceivable that some link in this chain of reactions involving enzymes, cofactors, pH, etc., is affected by the quantitative insufficiency of a single set of chromosomes. We need more data.

Another question that arises upon perusal of Table 3 concerns the nature of the effect of a set of foreign chromosomes introduced by cross fertilization. A comparison of items 3 and 2 in the table shows that a gynogenetic haploid is capable of more development than the correspond-

TABLE 3

Type of embryo	♀ cyto-plasm	♀ haploid chromo-some sets	♂ haploid chromo-some sets	Method of production	Development in *R.pip.* × *R.syl.*
1. Normal diploid	A	1A	1A	Normal fertilization	99–100% normal development to adult
2. Diploid hybrid	A	1A	1B	Cross fertilization	Block at early gastrula
3. Gynogenetic haploid	A	1A	0	(a) Chemical treatment of sperm (b) X-irradiation of sperm	Die as early tadpoles; never reach adult stage
4. Androgenetic haploid	A	0	1A	(a) Radiation of egg nucleus (b) Removal of egg nucleus	Die as early tadpoles; never reach adult stage
5. Androgenetic haploid hybrid	A	0	1B	Remove egg nucleus after fertilization with foreign sperm	Do not develop as well as 3 and 4, but live longer than 2 in *pipiens* × *catesbeiana* cross

ing diploid hybrid. The former develops to post-neurula stages and eventually succumbs to the haploid syndrome of abnormalities. The diploid hybrid in this particular interspecific cross, on the other hand, becomes arrested, blocked, at early gastrula. Thus, as Moore has noted, "the foreign sperm in this hybrid combination is acting as a 'poison.'" The same writer goes on to say that "The *sylvatica* chromosomes are acting in a genetically different cytoplasm and their activity might be using up limited substrates or result in the production of abnormal substances, which would act as competitive metabolites to the normal gene products, or even as poisons." We shall return to this point later when we discuss the application of the serial nuclear transplantation method to the hybrid problem.

The development of androgenetic haploid hybrids (item 5) as compared with haploids (items 3 and 4) and diploid hybrids (item 2) is of interest. As is perhaps to be expected, the androgenetic haploid hybrids do not develop as far as an ordinary haploid. In fact, in this particular cross, the haploid hybrids do not develop beyond late blastula stage. The same is true for the androgenetic haploid hybrid between *pipiens* and *catesbeiana,* and in this cross it was noted that these androgenetic haploid hybrids survive longer in the arrested state than do diploid hybrids made by simple cross fertilization. These facts again suggest some sort of competitive inhibition in the two sets of incompatible chromosomes—but not for simple energy sources, for all these hybrids cytolyze when there is still an abundance of yolk in their cells.

Another way of looking at the hybrid problem has been expressed [28]. "The effect of hybridity is then a loss of control over development. Certain tendencies, located in the cytoplasm of the egg, are not balanced by the hybrid nucleus, and the tendencies are even less balanced by the sperm nucleus alone."

If we think in terms of competition among gene products, there is some evidence (not presented in the table) that these necessary gene products are diffusible, or at least that they pass from cell to cell [27]. A mosaic embryo of *Bufo,* a toad, was triploid on one side and haploid on the other. This mosaic developed to an adult which still had haploid tissues. In other words, the haploid cells did not die but were able to participate in development because of something received from the healthy triploid cells.

Among the significant general conclusions that can be drawn from the study of the development of hybrid embryos is that the genes, or rather their molecular representatives in the cytoplasm, have highly specific effects upon early developmental events. These gene products cannot be simple, nonspecific compounds that can enter into synthetic activities in *any* egg cytoplasm. If derived from too distantly related a species, little or no development will follow their introduction into a given egg cytoplasm.

This brings us now to the question of just what happens when chromosomes are obliged to replicate in foreign cytoplasm. Fortunately some excellent recent studies are available to shed light on this question. Before presenting these new data, however, the time has come to discuss some contemporary views as to the mode of chromosome replication.

CHROMOSOME REPLICATION AND THE SYNTHESIS OF DNA

The structural genes of the chromosomes are DNA molecules whose specificity resides in various sequences in arrangement of the bases. During growth (increase in cell number) there must obviously occur synthesis of DNA to provide the raw materials for the daughter chromosomes produced during each mitotic cycle (unless, of course, there is some preformed stockpile of DNA available in the cytoplasm to provide for synthesis of the new chromosomes). For many years, cytologists made use of the Feulgen stain for DNA to observe the changes in chromosome shape and behavior during mitosis and meiosis. Not until the 1940's and early 1950's, however, were methods available for quantitative measurements of DNA in nuclei. The cytophotometric methods devised are too complex with respect to instrumentation to be considered here in any detail. These methods depend upon the fact that the nucleic acids have a very high UV absorption at 2600 Å (= angstrom units), due to their content in purine and pyrimidine bases. By using a microscope with quartz lenses and prisms (which allow UV to pass through) and a source of UV light, the absorption of parts of a cell, such as a chromosome, could be determined photoelectrically.

Another method for following the synthesis of DNA quantitatively became available when radioisotopes began to be widely used [63]. When cells or tissues engaged in active cell division were exposed to radiophosphorus (P^{32}), the phosphorus was incorporated into the various phosphorus-containing molecules within the cells. After suitable chemical treatments of such cells after fixation to remove non-DNA phosphorus, the investigator obtained a slide of his tissue which could be covered with a sensitive film to detect the radiations emitted from the radiophosphorus-containing DNA. It should be added that once incorporated into DNA, the radiophosphorus stays there. That is, it has an exceedingly low rate of "turnover." The P^{32} isotope thus is a good marker for newly synthesized DNA.

It was found that all the DNA synthesis required for the next generation of daughter chromosomes occurred during the mitotic interphase—not during the prophase condensation of chromosomes that is seen with ordinary nuclear stains. The next problem was to find out how this synthesis of DNA was related to the duplication of chromosomes. It was first determined that synthesis of the *protein* parts of the chromosomes coincided in time with the interphase synthesis of DNA.

We will describe here one ingenious method devised to observe directly and simultaneously both DNA synthesis and the duplication of chromosome during mitosis [63]. Here again autoradiography was employed, this time the isotope of hydrogen called tritium being the label chosen. This tritium was introduced into the DNA of plant cells by growing bean seedlings in solutions containing tritium-labeled thymidine, one of the basic components of the DNA molecule. The thymidine was rapidly built into the chromosomal DNA being synthesized at the time of exposure to the isotope, and it stayed there when the seedlings were

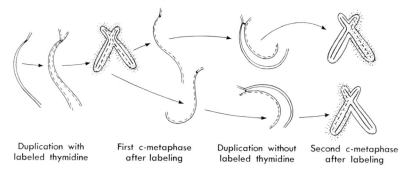

| Duplication with labeled thymidine | First c-metaphase after labeling | Duplication without labeled thymidine | Second c-metaphase after labeling |

FIGURE 24. Organization and mode of replication of chromosome components as proposed by Taylor. Solid lines represent nonlabeled units; dashed lines indicate radioactively labeled units. The dots represent grains in the autoradiographs. A c-metaphase is that stage of mitosis brought about by the drug colchicine, which blocks cell divisions but does not interfere with duplication of chromosomes. (Taylor, 1957.)

transferred out of the isotope solution into ordinary culture medium. Now any new chromosomal DNA synthesized would not be labeled. Only the chromosomes formed during the period of exposure to the isotope would bear the radioactive label. The descendants of the labeled chromosomes had then to be observed for presence or absence of the label and its distribution among them.

Some means of determining how many times the labeled parent chromosomes had duplicated had to be found. This was achieved by transferring the seedlings into a colchicine solution, which blocks cell divisions but does not interfere with duplication of chromosomes. If 12 is the usual number of chromosomes in these plant cells, then chromosomes in cells with 24 or 48 chromosome complements must have duplicated one time or two times, respectively.

The results of autoradiographs of the daughter chromosomes of the first two "generations" after labeling are shown in Fig. 24. Each chromosome consists of two strands. When these duplicated in the presence of the label, each of the two daughter chromosomes was equally labeled. After one duplication in absence of the label each daughter chromosome produced a labeled and a nonlabeled descendant. After two duplications in absence of labeled precursors, one in every four daughter chromosomes was labeled. We may disregard here the complication introduced by exchanges of short regions between labeled and nonlabeled sister chromosomes; such exchanges merely serve to prove the point.

Let us quote from the original report of this work [63]: "We interpret these findings to mean that the chromosomes before duplication are composed of two units which extend throughout the length of the chromosome. The units separate at duplication time and each has a complementary unit built alongside it. Each pair of complementary units appears as a uniformly and equally labeled daughter chromosome at the following division. However, each chromosome must be composed of an original non-labeled unit and a new labeled unit as revealed by its subsequent behavior. At the next duplication the labeled unit separates from its non-labeled complement and has a non-labeled unit built alongside it. This results in a labeled daughter chromosome. . . . The other unit must not have been labeled, for it produces a daughter chromosome completely free of label."

More experiments must be made on different materials and more time must elapse before it can be decided that this is the universal mode of chromosome duplication. Nonetheless it seems safe to conclude that in this material at least, "the original and new DNA are distinct entities, the integrity of which is conserved during replication." It remains to be discovered how the DNA molecules are arranged together with other molecules to form the structural units of the chromosomes—for the chromosome is several orders of magnitude larger than the strands of DNA being studied by chemists and virologists.

Among these workers, as of this writing there appears to be fairly general agreement that replication of the DNA molecule requires that the two-stranded helix of the parent molecule unwinds, following which each strand then serves as a template for the formation of a complementary strand [21, 24]. Thus one parent strand would appear in each of the two daughter molecules at first generation. At second generation, only one-quarter of the daughter molecules would contain a parent strand, the rest being new. Even the recent discovery of a strain of bacteriophage whose genetic material consists of a single-stranded form of DNA has not upset this basic hypothesis. It appears likely that the replicative cycle of this aberrant virus involves a double-stranded stage [58].

CHROMOSOME REPLICATION IN HYBRID EMBRYOS

After this brief excursion into some recent studies on the manner of chromosome replication, let us return to the specific situation in which chromosomes are required to replicate in foreign cytoplasm. We have already discussed the developmental difficulties encountered by several types of hybrid embryos. It occurred to several investigators that the technique of nuclear transplantation might be applied with profit to the problems raised by hybrid embryos. We will choose as our illustration again the familiar cross of *Rana pipiens* female × *Rana sylvatica* male as reported by Moore [49].

A *Rana sylvatica* ovum, fertilized with *pipiens* sperm, is enucleated. This androgenetic hybrid is allowed to develop to the mid-blastula stage. By this time the *pipiens* nucleus has undergone about twelve mitotic divisions or chromosome replications. Although we are speaking in terms of a single operation, actually dozens of such nuclear transplantations had to be made. During these "divisions" the original *pipiens* chromosomes had to replicate at the expense of whatever substrates were available in the *sylvatica* egg cytoplasm. Have the *pipiens* genes been able to duplicate themselves exactly in this alien territory? Apparently not, because when one such *"pipiens"* nucleus from the blastula stage is transferred back into what should be its species-specific cytoplasmic environment (an enucleated *pipiens* egg), development proceeds only as far as the beginning of gastrulation.

Following these first experiments on the effects of transferring nuclei from one species to another and back again, Fischberg and his associates used the same method with some different species. These workers obtained results similar to those obtained with *Rana*, but they also asked one further interesting question. Will a nucleus that has been altered when it undergoes mitosis in the cytoplasm of a different species become more normal if it is returned to the cytoplasm of its own species and allowed to undergo repeated mitoses?

To answer this question it is necessary to make repeated back-transfers of the altered nuclei into enucleated ova of their own original species. The evidence from the several laboratories where this kind of work has been undertaken is still somewhat conflicting. Perhaps the weight of evidence at the time of writing is on the side of failure to produce any improvement in development by successive back-transfers of nuclei to their own cytoplasm. Thus the original alteration of the chromosomes replicating in foreign cytoplasm appears to be irreversible when this is the test situation. It would be interesting to see whether such chromosomes could form normal replicas of themselves "from scratch" when offered the four bases needed to construct DNA.

The species pairs involved in these experiments are only remotely related in the genetic and taxonomic sense. Thus one must ask whether nuclei can be transferred between closely related species and subspecies and still show their specific characteristics unmodified by the less foreign cytoplasm. Such experiments have been carried out in several laboratories, and the answer is in the affirmative.

As Moore has pointed out: "With more work on pairs of species, we might anticipate a spectrum of results—from the extensive modifications of nuclei in exchanges between remotely related species, to some modification in exchanges between more closely related species, to no modification in even more closely related species and subspecies." Whether or not such a spectrum of results will be obtained depends in part upon the willingness of new, young investigators to undertake the exacting and time-consuming work involved in such studies.

THE MOLECULAR BASIS FOR DEVELOPMENTAL ARREST IN HYBRID EMBRYOS

Meanwhile there are fascinating problems to be attacked at the biochemical level concerning the nature of the molecular changes that occur in the *R. pipiens* nuclei replicating in *R. sylvatica* cytoplasm. On the basis of some already established facts concerning DNA content and synthesis in frog eggs, an hypothesis has been advanced [49] concerning the molecular basis for a genetic change during chromosome replication.

We have had occasion in an earlier section to refer to the three-year period that a frog oocyte spends in the maternal ovary before it reaches maturity. Among the many synthetic activities going on during this time is the formation and storage of large quantities of cytoplasmic DNA. If this DNA is synthesized under the control of specific "structural genes," it is reasonable to suppose that the cytoplasmic DNA will possess a specificity determined by the nucleus of the growing oocyte. Presumably the specificity resides in the base sequences within the DNA molecules.

The actual quantity of the cytoplasmic DNA is both impressive and significant. Although the several quantitative determinations do not agree at all well, those workers who have made chemical determinations for cytoplasmic DNA in the mature oocyte or ovum agree that there is enough for at least 2000 and possibly as many as 25,000 diploid nuclei. If the latter figure is close to the actual amount, there is more than enough for the estimated 10,000 cells in the mid-blastula. There is little or no *de novo* synthesis of DNA in cleavage and blastula stages. Finally, it has been found that when *sylvatica* chromosomes replicate in *pipiens* cytoplasm, the nuclei contain normal, or nearly normal, *amounts* of DNA. This indicates that the *sylvatica* chromosomes are using components of the foreign cytoplasm to build up copies of themselves.

Putting these several facts together, Moore has suggested that "copy errors" are made when the *pipiens* chromosomes replicate themselves from the *sylvatica* cytoplasmic DNA. Returned to the *pipiens* cytoplasm, the modified nuclei can no longer use *pipiens* cytoplasmic DNA to make entirely normal *pipiens* chromosomes.

It will occur to you that the validity of this hypothesis depends in part upon whether cytoplasmic DNA can be used "as such" for chromosome replication. If so, specific base sequences ("the code," in current parlance) inappropriate to the other member of the species pair could be picked up and built into the transferred nuclei during chromosome replication. If, on the other hand, the cytoplasmic DNA must be broken down into individual bases for chromosomal replication there would appear to be no reason why the transplanted chromosomes cannot make use of these small molecules to construct normal replicas of themselves. The evidence applying to this question is as yet incomplete.

The implications of these interesting studies are far-reaching and raise many new problems for experimental attack. That a genetic change in a nucleus can occur as a result of the specific composition of the surrounding cytoplasm now appears highly probable from these studies and from the "nuclear differentiation" experiments discussed earlier. In the case of nuclear differentiation of, say, an endoderm cell, there have been no studies as yet to indicate the molecular basis for the genetic change hypothesized. The hybrid studies implicate base sequences of DNA. But we have as yet no reason to assume that normal cellular differentiation similarly involves the same kind of changes in "code" in chromosomal DNA as a result of differences among cytoplasmic nucleic acid precursors in various regions of the egg. Changes in gene function do not necessarily imply alteration of the structural gene *per se*.

There are other ways in which gene function can be altered independently of actual "copying errors" during replication of chromosomal DNA. It must also be recognized that the frog ovum is rather exceptional in its high content of cytoplasmic DNA. *Acetabularia*, on the other hand, lacks any measurable trace of cytoplasmic DNA, whereas it does contain RNA, which plays a controlling role in synthesis of cytoplasmic proteins. The "cap-forming substances" of *Acetabularia* also are species specific, presumably as a result of base sequences of RNA, possibly of nuclear origin. One would like to know the actual molecular composition of the cytoplasmic RNA in both the normal and "hybrid" eggs and in *Acetabularia* interspecies grafts.

Studies of the DNA composition of *heterochromatin* in normal and hybrid embryos are needed also. This material, largely empty of genes, does affect expression of genes of the euchromatic regions of chromosomes. The DNA content of the heterochromatic parts of chromosomes has been found to vary in some plant cells as a result of an environmental factor, exposure to cold. There is some evidence that the DNA of heterochromatin is more labile than in euchromatin. In any case, it has been known for some years that heterochromatin is involved in the so-called "position effect" in which genes are transferred to new neighborhoods within a chromosome as a result of chromosomal aberrations such as translocation and inversion. The nearness of a given gene locus to heterochromatin determines the extent to which the gene action is modified as an accompaniment of rearrangements between heterochromatin and euchromatin.

The possibility should be considered that when chromosomes replicate in foreign cytoplasm, the composition of their heterochromatin is altered, and that these changes in turn affect the activities of the "structural genes" *per se*. Thus even assuming that the hypothesis is validated that the actual DNA molecules of the hybrid are altered, there still remains a large gap between this "cause" and its effects upon development. It should be kept in mind that in these studies, as well as in the nuclear differentiation studies, the genetic changes demonstrated result in blocks to development, failures in normal differentiation. What we really want to know eventually is whether and in what manner genetic changes have *positive* effects in bringing about normal development and cellular differentiation.

With respect to the problem of the molecular basis for developmental arrest in hybrids, the serial nuclear transplantation studies present a new challenge. It is to be hoped that micromethods will be devised and applied to determine the base ratios and sequences in normal and hybrid nucleic acid fractions. Such a technique utilizing microelectrophoresis already has been devised and applied to the giant chromosomes of salivary gland cells of the insect larva [7]. We know already that the hybrid embryo of *pipiens* × *sylvatica* continues to synthesize DNA after its development has blocked. Now we can add that this DNA probably is abnormal in composition. We know also that although the hybrid nuclei are overloaded with RNA, the cytoplasm apparently cannot utilize the hybrid type of RNA. If the abnormal nucleus has not altered the cytoplasm prior to the stage of block, one might perhaps look forward to such possibilities as supplying the blocked hybrid with RNA from a normal embryo and obtaining further development.

10

Molecular Genetics and the Embryo

Some beginnings have been made in the attempt to apply to embryos what has been learned in recent years concerning gene action in control of the synthesis of specific proteins in bacteria and viruses. There are many links in the postulated chain of reactions in microorganisms, and embryos are in general more difficult to handle experimentally. Nonetheless, when technical difficulties have been overcome, it is to be anticipated that the embryo will be shown to employ patterns for nucleo-cytoplasmic control of specific protein synthesis similar to those found in microorganisms. Even then, the embryo still will present unique problems at its higher level of organization. We will mention several such problems after first outlining briefly some contemporary schemes concerning genetic control of protein synthesis [40, 41]. The synthesis of protein molecules is basic to the formation of all the other molecules manufactured by the cell. Many of these proteins are enzymes required to build up carbohydrates, fats, sterols, organic acids and bases, and so on—the raw materials for cellular structure and function.

GENETIC CONTROL OF THE SYNTHESIS OF SPECIFIC PROTEINS

Some elements of the process of protein synthesis as it is understood at the moment of writing are diagrammed in Fig. 25. Ultimate control over the synthesis of specific proteins resides in deoxynucleic acid (DNA), the material of the structural genes. By this it is meant that the molecular organization of all the proteins characteristic of any organism at a given time in its life cycle is dictated and limited in the final analysis by the composition of its structural genes. The specificity of the structural genes is determined by the linear order of the four bases which combined with deoxyribose and phosphate comprise the DNA molecules.

The actual sites of protein synthesis are located at the cytoplasmic bodies known as ribosomes. Three kinds of ribonucleic acids (RNA) are involved in the intervening processes between structural gene and protein synthesis at the ribosomes. All three presumably are made at the expense of a pool of nucleotide precursors. For a given gene, a messenger RNA (mRNA) is produced, which is probably a polyribonucleotide. This mRNA becomes associated with the ribosomes of the cytoplasm.

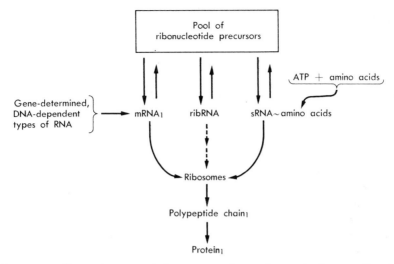

FIGURE 25. Some elements of the process of protein synthesis according to a contemporary scheme. (Adapted from Jacob and Wollman, reference 41.)

The ribosomes contain a second type of RNA (ribRNA) which also was formed from pooled precursors and whose character is determined by the structural genes.

The amino acid components for the proteins reach the ribosomal sites for assembly into polypeptide chains in an energy-rich form. The third type of RNA, known as soluble RNA (sRNA), is involved in the transfer of such activated, energy-rich amino acids ($\sim$amino acids) to the ribosomes. Soluble RNA is specific both as to the amino acid carried and the site of the mRNA to which it attaches. The ultimate source of the energy for activation is adenosine triphosphate (ATP), which has been shown to provide energy for many other cell activities in addition to the one under discussion here.

The amino acids are assembled then into polypeptide chains under the direction of the mRNA which was derived from DNA of a given structural gene. Once formed, the polypeptide chains fold to form Protein₁ and become detached from the ribosomes. Presumably the latter now are free to receive new mRNA of the same or of a different composition.

The arbitrariness with which the above statements are made requires a word of caution. Information in this area of research is moving so rapidly that there is bound to be some temporary disagreement as to details among the various investigators involved. The essence of the matter, however, is that all investigators agree that there is nuclear-cytoplasmic transfer of molecules which carry specificity to sites of protein synthesis, and that the primary specificity is localized in segments

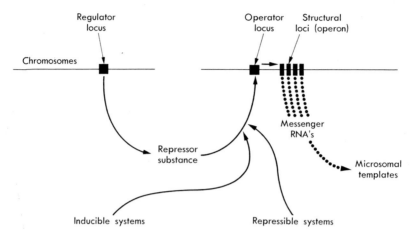

FIGURE 26. The hypothetical scheme of Jacob and Monod to explain genetic control of specific protein synthesis in the cytoplasm. (Waddington, 1962.)

of nuclear DNA which are defined as structural genes. There is further agreement that all types of RNA formed by a cell are determined by DNA.

The ribosomes or microsomes engaged in protein synthesis are localized on cytoplasmic fine structures, membranes, the two elements together being termed "ergastoplasm" by some workers. There is then a growing tendency to consider that the microsomal "machinery" synthesizes a new specific protein because it receives new specific and short-lived "messenger" RNA, which changes the specific activity of already existing microsomes.

The sequence of reactions does not end here. The structural gene itself, according to a scheme worked out by Jacob and Monod [41] for the colon bacillus E. coli, is controlled by an "operator" gene (Fig. 26). The operator gene is under the control of a "regulator gene." Operator and regulator genes are thought to function in suppressing the activity of their corresponding structural genes. Thus it is supposed that the regulator gene produces a repressor substance which specifically inhibits the functioning of the operator gene. Production of the corresponding mRNA thus is blocked. This block is sometimes referred to as "turning off a gene."

The question then becomes: What regulates the activity of the regulator? The answer proposed by Jacob and Monod is that cytoplasmic substances (of unspecified nature as yet but possibly small molecular weight metabolites) modify the character of the repressor substances produced by the regulator gene. These modified repressor substances are not able to repress the operator's activity, the theory continues. Therefore the particular segments of DNA under control of a specific operator gene can function to set in motion the subsequent steps of transferring their "code" via messenger RNA to sites of protein synthesis in the cytoplasm, the ribosomal particles.

It should be realized that the various elements of this model system were postulated on the basis of very extensive experiments with wild-type and mutant strains of the bacterium *E. coli*. This organism exhibits more clearly than most other organisms studied to date two fundamental phenomena: enzyme induction and enzyme repression. The former occurs when bacteria are placed in a medium containing a substrate, a metabolite, for whose breakdown the bacterium possesses a specific enzyme. Within a few minutes after addition of the "inducer" metabolite the enzyme begins to be synthesized at a rapid rate and may increase in some instances from an estimated one molecule of enzyme per cell to 1000 molecules per cell. This induced enzyme synthesis ceases when the inducer is removed.

Enzyme repression is observed when the bacteria are presented with a product which they normally synthesize via a series of linked enzyme reactions. For example, if compound E is the end product of reactions $A \rightarrow B \rightarrow C \rightarrow D \rightarrow E$, each step under control of a specific enzyme, addition of E to the medium causes repression of the activities of all four enzymes [31].

We are greatly oversimplifying our exposition of the scheme of Jacob and Monod, because for a complete treatment of the topic it would be necessary to go into the details of many experiments in bacterial genetics. All we should like to ask here is whether this conceptual scheme suggests new ways of looking at nucleocytoplasmic relations in developing systems such as the embryo.

GENETIC CONTROL IN CELLULAR DIFFERENTIATION

In the first place, because many steps intervene between regulator gene and final synthesis of specific enzyme protein (or repression of such synthesis), the scheme offers great flexibility, i.e., opportunity for origin of new substances.

There are several points at which gene action itself could be modified in either a quantitative or qualitative manner. It is conceivable also that changes at the level of sRNA will change the arrangement of the amino acids brought for assembly to the ribosomal sites and that these changes could occur in various regions at various stages of development. This would follow if nuclear differentiation occurs and gives rise to ˗˗ges in sRNA, as has been hypothesized for certain types of genetic

Let us take a specific example of differentiation of a given cell type, striated muscle, within the developing embryo. Of the characteristic muscle proteins let us single out myosin and formulate the circumstances for its synthesis in terms of the Jacob-Monod scheme. The structural gene loci concerned with production of messenger RNA's for myosin synthesis may be presumed to be present in the nuclei of all cells of the early embryo. At some point in time, the cytoplasm of cells in the axial mesoderm (but not in the intermediate or lateral mesoderm, or any other region for that matter) has become different from other cytoplasms. Recall that the cytoplasm already is heterogeneous even in the unfertilized ovum of the frog, and these cytoplasmic differences may be presumed to have been amplified gradually during development from fertilization up to the time of primary mesodermal differentiation.

As a result of such cytoplasmic differences in the modified presumptive muscle cell cytoplasm, the regulator gene is inactivated and fails to produce the repressor substance required to put the operator locus for myosin structural genes out of action. In the cytoplasm of another cell type (endoderm, for example), this specific regulator gene continues to be active, while some other regulator gene(s) is(are) suppressed and the way is cleared for action of structural genes to produce messenger RNA's for the synthesis of types of proteins characteristic of liver or pancreas.

Basically the whole scheme invokes a controlling role for nonchromosomal (possibly cytoplasmic) substances which prevent the regulator genes from producing a specific kind of repressor substance. These as yet undefined substances come to have a differential distribution, availability or activity among the cytoplasms of the cells derived by cleavage from the original egg cytoplasm, itself heterogeneous in many kinds of eggs.

That genes exist which can control the activities of other genes as in the operator-structural gene relationship has been confirmed in higher organisms as well as in bacteria. In maize, the color pattern of the corn kernels is due to controlling genes that appear to affect the structural genes that are responsible for production of the characteristic pigments [46].

Already, then, we have two postulated steps at which control can be exercised over those genes that are most active at a given time and location within a developing system. (1) Regulator genes affect operator genes because the regulators are active in the presence of a specific (cytoplasmic?) substance. (2) Operator genes may control the activity of a whole battery of structural gene loci. In this scheme, genes become active because their activity ceases to be repressed. There is no *a priori* reason to suppose, however, that a regulator gene represses *only* one group of structural gene loci. Several active sites of structural genes might be freed simultaneously to produce messenger RNA's for several types of proteins. These messenger RNA's then might be forced to compete among one another for space along the microsomal surfaces [67]. The scheme thus acquires another dimension of flexibility.

THE CONCEPT OF COMPETITION IN THEORIES OF DEVELOPMENT

The concept of competition is by no means novel in theories of differentiation proposed in the past. Some of the earlier theories [20] proposed that competition among various regions for substances necessary for development occurred as a result of initially purely quantitative differences in the several parts of the egg. Gradients in rate of metabolism (oxygen consumption) would furnish examples of such quantitative differences. A region with a higher rate of oxygen consumption would compete more successfully for substances needed for development and use up such substances at the expense of other regions.

Simple quantitative differences *must* be invoked in the origin of cytoplasmic differences in such an egg as that of the brown marine alga *Fucus,* where polarity of the initially homogeneous egg cytoplasm can be determined by gradients in temperature, pH, carbon dioxide, exposure to ultraviolet light, and so on (Fig. 27).

Another type of competition based upon initially qualitative differences among parts of the egg was proposed in the double gradient theory of Dalcq and Pasteels [38]. Here two hypothetical factors located in egg cortex and yolk respectively were assumed to be distributed in gradient fashion, with one factor (C) having its highest concentration at the animal pole of the egg, the other (V) falling off in concentration along the vegetal-animal axis. Interplay of these two factors at various levels of the egg axis would give rise to quantitative differences in concentration of still a third hypothetical factor or compound, "organisine." Different concentrations of this agent in the various regions were proposed as the basis for all the qualitative differences that arise during development. Demonstration that the cell cortex of the gray crescent region contains factors that induce a secondary embryo when the cortex is grafted to another egg lends support to the "C factor" of this theory, which was based originally upon the results of centrifuging early embryos. Recent studies on the fine structure and biochemistry of amphibian yolk platelets [74] may lead to specification of the hypothetical "V factor(s)" of the theory.

Later competition theories have reflected the increasing understanding of the manner in which nuclear genes control the synthesis of specific cytoplasmic proteins. These more contemporary theories are lineal descendants, however, of a theory originally formulated by Driesch, a contemporary of Weismann, in 1894. Driesch, and later (1934) T. H. Mor-

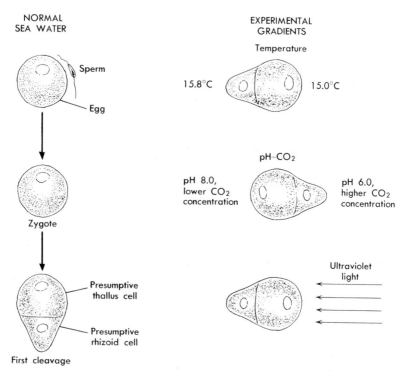

NORMAL
SEA WATER

EXPERIMENTAL
GRADIENTS

Temperature

Sperm

Egg

15.8°C   15.0°C

Zygote

pH–CO₂

pH 8.0,
lower CO₂
concentration

pH 6.0,
higher CO₂
concentration

Presumptive
thallus cell

Ultraviolet
light

Presumptive
rhizoid cell

First cleavage

FIGURE 27. An egg of the marine alga, *Fucus furcatus*, undergoing its first stage of differentiation. About 17 hours after fertilization, eggs kept at 15°C develop a protuberance at one side which later is separated by the plane of first cleavage from the rest of the egg. This protuberance cell after further divisions gives rise to the rhizoid (rootlike structure of the alga), while the other cell develops into the main body, or thallus. In the figure the direction of outgrowth of the protuberance is shown in eggs that have developed after fertilization in the presence of imposed gradients in temperature, pH-CO_2 concentration, and the shorter wavelengths of visible light. The diameter of the egg is approximately 0.1 mm. (Whitaker, 1940.)

gan, pointed out that although the nuclei resulting from cleavage of the egg may be equipotential, they become distributed among regions of the egg that, in many eggs at least, differ in chemical composition and cytoplasmic organization. As a result of such cytoplasmic heterogeneity, genes might be activated in some nuclei and inactivated in others [50].

Although many years were to elapse before direct experimental proof of genetic control of enzyme synthesis and activity was obtained [6], Driesch proposed that differences in enzyme activity resulted from the differential activation or inactivation of genes residing in different cytoplasmic territories of the egg. Thus would follow the origin of new specific cytoplasms.

It is not feasible here to mention the names of all the workers whose experiments and thinking have advanced this area of investigation so rapidly during the past two decades. The Caspersson and Brachet theories of protein synthesis were enormous stimulants to other workers. The flowering of chemical genetics, especially in microorganisms and viruses, rapid growth in purely biochemical studies of the reactions among ultracentrifugable fractions of cells, techniques of electron microscopy and autoradiography—all are included in the background for such contemporary formulations as Waddington's adaptation of the Jacob-Monod scheme to the interpretation of nucleocytoplasmic interactions in differentiating cells.

CYTOPLASMIC GENES: SOME HYPOTHESES

We should, however, mention another theoretical construct whose controversial nature has spurred a number of experiments and hypotheses. At least as early as 1945 the suggestion had been put forth that genes directly produce substances which are replicas of themselves in most respects, and that these replicas pass into the cytoplasm where they control synthetic processes [66]. These cytoplasmic representatives of the gene came to be called plasmagenes, with the important qualification that they were *gene-initiated* "plasmagenes." This distinction had to be made when other self-replicating cytoplasmic particles independent of nuclear genes were described in certain protozoans, yeasts, and unicellular plants.

When first introduced into the field of differentiation, the idea of plasmagenes had some attractive features to embryologists. In primary induction, for example, it could be hypothesized that a population of plasmagenes specific for the production of neural-type cytoplasmic proteins was either activated, released, or suddenly induced to replicate when archenteron roof came to underly presumptive neural plate. Daughter cells would receive their share of such specific plasmagenes, which would continue to replicate themselves over successive cell generations [3]. According to this conceptual scheme, once a neural cell, never again an epidermal cell would be the dictum.

Whether or not differentiation is reversible still is a moot question among embryologists. Certainly some cells remain totipotent throughout the life cycle (the epidermis cells of *Begonia*, for example). Secondly, descendants of the original "neural" cell gradually diverge from one another to produce the multitude of different kinds of nerve cells found in the adult organism. Thus, increasing specialization of populations of plasmagenes is called for. Does this "stepwise" differentiation of postulated plasmagene populations involve alternative, dichotomous pathways, which, once selected, cannot be reversed? Or, from a new point of view recently proposed [5], are the changes basic to cell specialization sequential in character and thus more likely to be capable of reversibility?

In order to interpret increasing specialization among cell types according to the plasmagene theory, one would need to add the further assumption either that plasmagenes themselves differentiate, transform in type of specificity, or that there are populations of plasmagenes which compete among one another for precursors, the outcome of the competition depending upon nongenic, cytoplasmic factors or conditions.

For these reasons, among others, the idea of gene-initiated plasmagenes has been more favorably received than the alternative of relatively autonomous populations of cytoplasmic particles replicating themselves in the cytoplasm. As Waddington [66, p. 402] has said: "We are already faced with the difficulty of accounting for this progressive series of changes in a system one of whose major components consists of genes which we believe to retain their identity throughout. The difficulty is only made the greater if we have to suppose that the major factors in the cytoplasm also retain their identity."

NUCLEOCYTOPLASMIC INTERACTIONS REEXAMINED

During the few years that have elapsed since the above statement was made, major advances in molecular genetics have made possible a tentative reinterpretation of the older plasmagene hypothesis. In the older hypothesis, the burden of explanation for the replication of likeness falls upon cytoplasmic factors possessing the ability to produce more of their own kind. Thus a presumptive epidermis cell, having been exposed to a neuralizing agent, will possess plasmagenes which replicate and are distributed during each mitotic division so that both daughter cells receive plasmagenes that determine "neural" characters.

In view of the newer concepts derived from molecular genetics, however, it would be postulated that such a neuralizing agent releases or activates cytoplasmic compounds which control the activity of operator and therefore of structural gene loci. Persistence of the new type of differentiation thus initiated would depend upon a continuous supply of regulatory substances from the cytoplasm in order to maintain a persisting specific type of regulation of structural gene action.

Elements of this scheme have been "in the air" for a number of years, but the necessary specific biochemical knowledge (such as evidence) for all RNA being DNA dependent was lacking to permit naming of the actual compounds involved and the nature of their interactions. For example, Goldschmidt in the 1920's postulated that there exists between each gene and its appropriate cytoplasmic "substrate" a "lock-and-key" specificity such that a given gene is inactive except in the presence of the cytoplasmic constituent whose stereochemical configurations match those of the gene [30]. The "lock-and-key" concept arose in association with advances in immunology, one of the first areas of biological specificity to be explored.

Wright [71, 72] saw the activity of the genes during development as being dependent upon the physical and chemical environment in the cell —an environment for which the genes themselves are largely responsible. A sort of cyclical feedback occurs, he postulated, between genome and its ever-changing chemical environment, so that the changing interactions between gene and environment provide the motive power for driving embryonic cells along their diverse paths of differentiation. Somewhat later we find Brachet [12] stating that these gene-initiated plasmagenes might act as intermediaries between the gene and the protein which is synthesized under its control, and be identical with ribonucleoprotein cytoplasmic particles.

The concept of ribosomal-stabilized messenger RNA's as described earlier in the chapter is perhaps the contemporary extension of the earlier gene-dependent plasmagene hypothesis. Furthermore, in the light of more recent investigations with microbial systems, it appears less likely that replication of such cytoplasmic bodies occurs. Rather, in contemporary schemes, cytoplasmic regulatory substances would be considered to evoke a continuous flow of messenger RNA's to account for persistence of cell types.

Waddington has visualized the general organization of gene-cytoplasm interactions in terms of a "double cycle" (Fig. 28). In one cycle, the cytoplasm affects the genes themselves in a feedback type of relationship that controls the rates at which different genes are acting. A second type of feedback control is exercised in the other postulated cycle, in which the cytoplasm affects gene-to-phenotype chain of reactions at some step *after* the gene has produced its first immediate product.

Considering the first kind of cycle in the light of the Jacob-Monod scheme, a given regulator gene produces a repressor substance which we may hypothesize is released into the cytoplasm. The cytoplasm also contains cytoplasmic regulatory substances of unknown biochemical nature. These cytoplasmic regulator substances acting through their appropriate operator genes determine whether or not a given structural (DNA) gene locus is active at a given time. Thus far neither postulated cycle specifies the biochemical composition of the substances involved. When we get to the next step the situation improves because, if we may consider

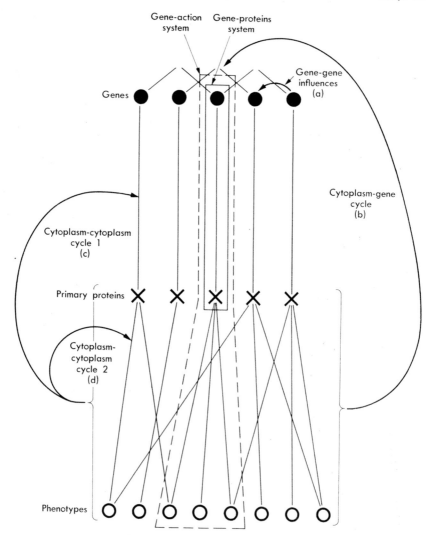

FIGURE 28. Scheme of Waddington to demonstrate possible types of nucleo-cytoplasmic interactions. Each gene determines the character of a primary protein; the primary proteins interact with one another to produce the final phenotype, the sum total of observable characteristics of the organism. The set of processes connecting a gene with a phenotypic character is called the gene-action system, outlined in bold dashes. The set of processes connecting the gene with its primary protein is called the gene-protein system, enclosed in the diagram in the elongated rectangle. The scheme of Jacob and Monod would apply to the gene-protein system. Interreactions in the Waddington scheme could occur at (a) gene to gene, (b) cytoplasm to gene, (c) cytoplasm to gene-protein system, (d) cytoplasm to primary-protein-to-phenotype processes. (Waddington, 1962.)

messenger RNA's as the genes' immediate and specific products, we can place them in Waddington's cytoplasm-to-cytoplasm cycles.

Proceeding now to the next postulated step, we invoke the function of messenger RNA in protein synthesis. A specific messenger RNA despatched from the nucleus associates with the ribosomal machinery of the ergastoplasm. Activated amino acids picked up meanwhile by sRNA are then linked together in the order specified by the modified ribosomal surface. A new type of protein is formed.

Between these primary proteins and the final visible and biochemical manifestions of a differentiated cell (phenotypes) lie many possible steps and interactions in Waddington's scheme. The postulated primary protein whose synthesis we have just traced probably is only one of a large number of proteins (enzymes) required for the synthesis of, let us say, actomyosin and the organization of the actomyosin molecules into fibrils of the muscle cell. In such a series of enzyme reactions, other cytoplasmic conditions and components could become controlling factors—even such simple ones as local pH; availability of an ion such as Mg^{++} required for a specific reaction; presence or absence of, or relative concentration of, some small molecular cofactor; level of energy production needed to drive reactions in a given direction.

An especially challenging problem of cell specialization arises in certain invertebrates. In the epithelio-muscular cells of *Hydra*, for example, different areas of the cytoplasm of a single cell differentiate in different manners. What kinds of simple gradients between different poles of a presumptive epithelio-muscular cell may be postulated to explain such intracellular differences?

In the course of the primary-protein-to-phenotype link, one might need to visualize the synthesis of quite ephemeral intermediaries that disappear because they are altered almost as soon as formed. One might also envisage the possibility that even fleeting changes in the configuration of a molecule (folding or unfolding; formation of new, temporary cross linkages between molecules) are of great significance—yet of such brief duration as to elude detection by contemporary biochemical methods.

One possible example of such an effect of change in configuration of a protein molecule upon its embryological behavior has been suggested. This is the effect of various durations of heating (which denatures proteins) upon the character of an inductor. Fresh bone marrow of the guinea pig, when sandwiched between two small pieces of presumptive epidermis of a newt early gastrula, causes the differentiation of such typically mesodermal structures as muscle, kidney, notochord, and blood cells—all characteristic of the trunk region of an intact embryo [73]. Thin layers of bone marrow tissue were steamed for very brief intervals before being sandwiched within the ectoderm pieces. As the duration of heating was extended from 25, 40, 60, through 150 seconds, the structures which later developed in the ectodermal sandwich became gradually modified away from mesodermal types of differentiation toward brain and various sense organs such as ear, eye, and nose. Yamada was tempted to assume "that the protein molecule responsible for induction goes through a series of changes in configuration . . . which are reflected in the regional effects." The bone marrow factor, however, may contain a population of different proteins with different heat-lability characteristics. Thus with different durations of heat treatment, different proteins might be inactivated to account for the changes in quality of induction.

Other steps between primary protein and phenotype might involve polymerization and conjugation between macromolecules. And even when we arrive at the proteins characteristic of a given cell type, this is still not the final phenotype. The various kinds of molecules are organized at a supramolecular level into structures of many different kinds and degrees of complexity, such as fibrils, granules, vacuoles, membranes, etc.

We have had occasion in earlier sections to refer to the well-known effects of specific cytoplasms of the egg (the ooplasms) upon differentiation in the presence of presumably totipotent nuclei. If the latter presumption is valid, is the effect of these different ooplasms at the level of the theoretical repressor substances in the Jacob-Monod scheme? Whatever the nature of these repressor substances, they must occur or arise so that de-inhibition of operator-to-structural genes occurs in such well-ordered sequences in time and place. The localization in the egg cortex of morphogenetically significant structures has been postulated many years ago as a result of experiments with centrifugation and has been verified by Curtis [22].

Another aspect of the time sequences characteristic of events during development is the fact that it is necessary to explain how one type of differentiation is "turned off" to give way to succeeding types. Messenger RNA's now are thought to be short-lived and readily destroyed unless stabilized by association with the ribosomes. The messengers, furthermore, are believed to be destroyed in the process of directing the assembly of amino acids on the ribosomal particles [41]. Thus, although the protein product of gene action may remain after its corresponding genes are "turned off," the messenger RNA's themselves are thought to be short-lived.

Another question suggested by the Jacob-Monod scheme is whether a messenger RNA from a specific kind of differentiated adult cell might be able to direct its specific type of protein synthesis in undifferentiated cells from an early gastrula? Several workers already have attempted to introduce microsomal fractions into eggs and into cells in tissue culture. The results thus far have been inconclusive. For example, it has been reported [8] that microsomes from adult kidney or liver when added to fibroblasts in tissue culture produce "nervelike" processes from these connective tissue cells. Cardiac muscle microsomes mixed with Roux sarcoma microsomes (to facilitate penetration into cells) and applied to the chorioallantoic membrane of the chick have been reported [25] to convert some of the epithelial membrane cells into "musclelike" elements, although contraction was not observed.

One might question, however, whether a cell from an early embryo has the competence, the cytoplasmic "machinery," to respond to adult types of mRNA, or whether it is too great a step to omit thus all the intermediary changes that would normally occur in the cytoplasm before the protein-synthesizing sites of early embryonic cells have matured and differentiated to that state at which they normally are exposed to specialized types of messenger RNA's. Perhaps messenger RNA from a just-determined area would be a better agent with which to confront an undifferentiated cytoplasm.

If one were to judge on the basis of electron microscope photographs of cells from early embryos of the "regulation" type such as the amphibian, it would appear that these cells may not be competent in the above sense of the term. These cells are deficient in ergastoplasm, the sites of protein synthesis, characteristic of adult cells. It is to be supposed that these cytostructures are both symptoms of differentiation and the means or machinery by means of which further differentiation is to be achieved. Another possibility has been suggested as a result of recent studies of unfertilized as compared with newly fertilized or activated eggs. It is suggested that the ribosomes of the unfertilized egg carry no "message" or that the mRNA is masked by a blocking layer of protein which is removed by the activation process [34, 65].

The reader should consult Waddington's [67] plates, which show beautiful photographs of the fine structure of developing cells. One most suggestive aspect of these photographs is the apparently close association between the nuclear envelope and the ergastoplasm. The latter may arise from outfoldings of the nuclear membrane, a situation that could provide a physical vehicle for passage of materials back and forth between nucleus and cytoplasmic areas.

There is no doubt that biologists are getting closer and closer to a complete understanding of the precise molecular machinery whereby specific proteins are synthesized. This is enormously encouraging to students of development, who may look forward in the perhaps not too far distant future to increased understanding of how an embryo goes about this job in its own well-organized way. The essential problems insofar as concerns the embryo are first, control of specific protein syntheses at the right time in the right place; and secondly, the mechanisms for organization of the proteins synthesized at increasing levels of complexity ranging from supramolecular fine structures, through cellular groupings to gross tissue and organ structures.

When some of these problems are better understood, we may then be in a better position to tackle once again with new viewpoints such long-standing embryological problems as the molecular basis for embryonic induction, the means of origin of polarity in an egg possessing no detectable initial polarity, and the way in which protein synthesis is controlled and modified in experimentally produced regulations of one half egg to form a whole embryo or two eggs fused to form one embryo. Perhaps the reader will be one of the contributors to this next phase of applying new concepts and techniques to very old problems in the study of development.

Summary

Summary

Let us round off our story by coming full circle back to the questions raised some seventy years ago by Weismann and his contemporaries. First, what has been added to the problem of continuity between generations? We have noted in an earlier chapter the technical difficulties involved in attempting to track the germ line from one generation to the next. We have described the most successful of such attempts to date, as a result of which it has been established that a particular region of amphibian egg cytoplasm becomes determined very early in development to be fated to become incorporated into primordial germ cells. This primordial germ cell cytoplasm appears to arise as one aspect of the activation process. True continuity of germ plasm between generations, however, is still unproven—and perhaps the question has been followed as far as it deserves for the time being. What has been proven is that somatic cell nuclei can be introduced into the germ line. As yet unresolved is the question whether germ-cell nuclei can participate not only in the differentiation of functional germ cells but also support differentiation of somatic cells.

As Ebert has written [25], the working hypothesis has shifted from the apparent contradiction between genetic constancy and the orderly establishment of populations of specialized, stable cells to: ". . . there are differential heterocatalytic activities of genetic materials depending on the type of cell in which they are located."

But what have the newer studies on the structure of the genetic material and its role in synthetic processes contributed to the basic problem? These studies provide new ways of looking at the control of gene action and the question of stability or mutability of the DNA sequences along the lengths of the DNA fibers. Waddington, for example, has made the fascinating suggestion that perhaps at the earliest stages of development, all genes are labile in the sequence of bases in the DNA molecule, and that later they become gradually stabilized by combination with molecules derived from the cytoplasm. He states that, "Although genes obviously have sufficient stability to be reliably transmitted through many generations . . . we need not feel ourselves bound to regard genes as nothing more than firmly bounded sequences of DNA, modifiable in no other way than by rare events of mutation." Perhaps a more concise restatement today would be that structural genes do indeed represent quite specific sequences of nucleotide bases within DNA molecules—but that differences in gene *action* occur as a result of cytoplasmic substances acting through regulator and operator loci.

The experiments described in Chapter 9 in which chromosomes were forced to replicate in foreign species cytoplasm, after which they were shown to have been modified from their original type, are consistent with the hypothesis suggested above. The evidence for gradual differentiation of many of the nuclei during early embryogenesis also applies here.

That nuclear differentiation accompanies cytoplasmic differentiation in some cells has been shown when the *activated egg cytoplasm* is host to the test nucleus. Cytoplasmic differentiation, however, can conceivably alter nuclear *function* without causing differentiation or mutation of structural genes. Expanding information and new concepts as to control of gene action both by cytoplasmic repressors and de-repressors and by other loci in the chromosomes makes it possible to conceive of ways in which genes can be activated and inactivated in various sequences during development of specific regions of the embryo and yet remain able to reproduce faithfully the entire genetic code in the presence of suitable cytoplasmic conditions.

Thus in the search for the origin of differences between cells, we are led back to the analysis of what is meant by suitable cytoplasmic conditions. By what means can an environmental factor such as a *differential* in temperature applied to an egg control the production or availability of cytoplasmic regulatory substances so as to determine the entire course of future development?

References

References

The references cited below comprise only a small fraction of the books, monographs, and original papers that were used in the preparation of the present text. We have avoided a prolific presentation of references and have used in many instances reviews and advanced textbooks which in themselves provide a rich mine of references to original papers and further reviews. In a minority of cases we have referred to the original journals in which the work was published because we wished to emphasize significant details that have not been presented critically in available review articles or texts.

This policy of economy necessarily has led to the omission of specific reference to very many of the investigators whose work is included in the present text. The interested student will find these references in the review articles and texts cited below.

1. ALLFREY, V. and A. E. MIRSKY, "How cells make molecules," *Scientific American,* **205,** 74–82 (1961).

2. BALINSKY, B. I., *An Introduction to Embryology,* Philadelphia: Saunders, 1960.

3. BARTH, LESTER G., *Embryology,* New York: Dryden Press, 1953.

4. BARTH, L. G. and LUCENA J. BARTH, *The Energetics of Development,* New York: Columbia University Press, 1954.

5. ——, "The relation between intensity of inductor and type of cellular differentiation of *Rana pipiens* presumptive epidermis." *Biol. Bull.,* **124,** 125–140 (1963).

6. BEADLE, G. W. and E. L. TATUM, in Sager, R. and F. J. Ryan, *Cell Heredity,* New York: Wiley, 1962, p. 29 *et seq.*

7. BEERMAN, W., "Cytological aspects of information transfer in cellular differentiation," *Amer. Zool.,* **3,** 23–32 (1963).

8. BENITEZ, H. H., M. R. MURRAY, and E. CHARGAFF, "Heteromorphic change of adult fibroblasts by ribonucleoprotein," *J. Biochem. Biophys. Cytol.,* **5,** 25–34 (1959).

9. BLACKLER, A. W., "Contribution to the study of germ-cells in the Anura," *J. Embryol. and Exptl. Morphol.,* **6,** 491–503 (1958).

10. BLACKLER, A. W. and M. FISCHBERG, "Transfer of primordial germ-cells in *Xenopus laevis,*" *J. Embryol. and Exptl. Morphol.,* **9,** 634–641 (1961).

11. BOUNOURE, L., "Recherches sur la lignée germinale chez la Grenouille rousse aux premiers stades du développement," *Ann. Sci. nat.,* **17,** 67–248 (1934).

12. BRACHET, J., *Biochemical Cytology,* New York: Academic Press, 1957.

13. ——, *The Biochemistry of Development,* New York: Pergamon Press, 1960.

14. ——, "Nucleic acids in development," *J. Cell. and Comp. Physiol.,* **60** suppl. 1, 1–18 (1962).

15. BRIGGS, R., "The influence of egg volume on the development of haploid and diploid embryos of the frog, *Rana pipiens,*" *J. Exptl. Zool.,* **111,** 255–294 (1949).

16. BRIGGS, R. W., E. U. GREEN, and T. J. KING, "An investigation of the capacity for cleavage and differentiation in *Rana pipiens* eggs lacking functional chromosomes," *J. Exptl. Zool.*, **116**, 455–500 (1951).

17. BRIGGS, R. and T. J. KING, "Factors affecting the transplantability of nuclei of frog embryonic cells," *J. Exptl. Zool.*, **122**, 485–506 (1953).

18. ——, "Nucleocytoplasmic interactions in eggs and embryos," *The Cell: Biochemistry, Physiology, Morphology*, Vol. I, J. Brachet and A. E. Mirsky, eds., New York and London: Academic Press, 1959, pp. 537–617. References to the earlier basic publications will be found here.

19. ——, "Nuclear transplantation studies on the early gastrula (*Rana pipiens*). I, Nuclei of presumptive endoderm," *Devel. Biol.*, **2**, 252–270 (1960).

19a. BRIGGS, R., THOMAS J. KING, and MARIE A. DiBERARDINO, "Development of nuclear-transplant embryos of known chromosome complement following parabiosis with normal embryos," *Symposium on Germ Cells and Development*, Institut Intern. d'Embryologie and Fondazione A. Baselli, 1960, pp. 441–477.

20. CHILD, C. M., *Patterns and Problems of Development*, Chicago: University of Chicago Press, 1941.

21. CRICK, F. H. C., "Nucleic acids," *Scientific American*, **197**, 188–203 (1957).

22. CURTIS, A. S. G., "Cortical grafting in *Xenopus laevis*," *J. Embryol. and Exptl. Morphol.*, **8**, 163–173 (1960).

23. DANIELLI, J. F., "The transfer of nuclei from cell to cell as a method of studying differentiation," *Exptl. Cell Research*, Suppl. 3, 98–101 (1955).

24. DELBRUCK, M. and G. S. STENT, "On the mechanism of DNA replication," in *The Chemical Basis of Heredity*, W. D. McElroy and B. Glass, eds., Baltimore: Johns Hopkins Press, 1957, pp. 699–736.

25. EBERT, JAMES D. and FRED H. WILT, "Animal viruses and embryos," *Quart. Rev. Biol.*, **35**, 261–312 (1960).

26. ELSDALE, T. R., M. FISCHBERG, and S. SMITH, "A mutation that reduces nucleolar number in *Xenopus laevis*," *Exptl. Cell Research*, **14**, 642–643 (1958).

27. FANKHAUSER, G., "The role of nucleus and cytoplasm," in *Analysis of Development*, B. H. Willier, P. A. Weiss, and V. Hamburger, eds., Philadelphia: Saunders, 1955.

28. FOWLER, J. A., "Anatomy and development of racial hybrids of *Rana pipiens*," *J. Morphol.*, **109**, 251–268 (1961).

29. GABRIEL, M. and S. FOGEL, eds., *Great Experiments in Biology*, Englewood Cliffs, New Jersey: Prentice-Hall, 1955.

30. GOLDSCHMIDT, R. B., *Theoretical Genetics*, Berkeley: University of California Press, 1955.

31. GORINI, L. and W. K. MAAS, "Feed-back control of the formation of biosynthetic enzymes," in *The Chemical Basis of Development*, W. D. McElroy and B. Glass, eds., Baltimore: Johns Hopkins Press, 1958.

32. GRANT, P., "Phosphate metabolism during oogenesis in *Rana temporaria*," *J. Exptl. Zool.*, **124**, 513–543 (1953).

33. GREGG, J. R., "Respiratory regulation in amphibian development," *Biol. Bull.*, **119**, 428–439 (1960).

34. GROSS, PAUL, Lecture at the Marine Biological Laboratory, Woods Hole, Mass., 1963.

35. GRÜNEBERG, HANS, *The Genetics of the Mouse*, Cambridge: Cambridge University Press, 1943.

36. GURDON, J. B., T. R. ELSDALE, and M. FISCHBERG, "Sexually mature individuals of *Xenopus laevis* from the transplantation of single somatic nuclei," *Nature, London*, **182**, 64–65 (1958).

37. HIMES, MARION M. and A. W. POLLISTER, "Symposium: Synthetic processes in the cell nucleus. V. Glycogen accumulation in the nucleus," *J. Histochem. and Cytochem.*, **10**, 175–185 (1962).

38. HOLTFRETER, J. and V. HAMBURGER, "Embryogenesis: Progressive differentiation," in *Analysis of Development*, B. H. Willier, Paul A. Weiss, and Viktor Hamburger, eds., Philadelphia: Saunders, 1955.

39. HUXLEY, JULIAN S. and G. R. DE BEER, *The Elements of Experimental Embryology*, Cambridge: Cambridge University Press, 1934.

40. JACOB, F. and J. MONOD, "Genetic regulatory mechanisms in the synthesis of proteins," *J. Molec. Biol.*, **3**, 318–356 (1961).

41. JACOB, F. and E. L. WOLLMAN, *Sexuality and the Genetics of Bacteria*, New York: Academic Press, 1961.

42. KEMP, N. E., "Electron microscopy of growing oocytes of *Rana pipiens*," *J. Biophys. Biochem. Cytol.*, **2**, 281–292 (1956).

43. KING, T. J. and R. BRIGGS, "Changes in the nuclei of differentiating gastrula cells, as demonstrated by nuclear transplantation," *Proc. Natl. Acad. Sci. U. S.*, **41**, 321–325 (1955).

44. KING, T. J. and R. BRIGGS, "Serial transplantation of embryonic nuclei," *Cold Spr. Harbor. Symp. Quant. Biol.*, **21**, 271–290 (1956).

45. LEHNINGER, A., "How cells transform energy," *Scientific American*, **205**, 63–73 (1961).

46. MCCLINTOCK, B., "Controlling elements and the gene," *Cold Spr. Harbor Symp. Quant. Biol.*, **21**, 197–216 (1956).

47. MCELROY, W. D. and B. GLASS, eds., *The Chemical Basis of Development*, Baltimore: Johns Hopkins Press, 1958.

48. MOORE, J. A., "Abnormal combinations of nuclear and cytoplasmic systems in frogs and toads," *Adv. in Genetics*, **7**, 139–182 (1955).

49. ——, "Nuclear transplantation and problems of specificity in developing embryos," *J. Cell. and Comp. Physiol.*, **60**, Suppl. 1, 19–34 (1962).

50. MORGAN, T. H., *Embryology and Genetics*, New York: Columbia University Press, 1934.

51. NIEUWKOOP, P. D., "Experimental investigations on the origin and determination of the germ cells, and on the development of the lateral plates and germ ridges in urodeles," *Arch. néerl. Zool.*, **8**, 1–205 (1946).

52. PARKES, A. S., U. FIELDING, and F. W. R. BRAMBELL, "Ovarian regeneration in the mouse after complete double ovariotomy," *Proc. Roy. Soc.*, **B 101**, 328–354 (1927).

53. PORTER, K. R., "Androgenetic development of the egg of *Rana pipiens*," *Biol. Bull.*, **77**, 233–257 (1939).

54. ROUX, WILHELM, "The problems, methods, and scope of developmental mechanics. An introduction to the "Archiv für Entwickelungsmechanik der Organismen," (translated from the German by Wm. M. Wheeler). Biological

Lectures at the Marine Biological Laboratory of Woods' Holl in the summer session of 1894. Boston: Ginn and Co., 1895. (This is still available in the M.B.L.'s reprint collection. The spelling of Woods Hole as given above is authentic for that time.)

55. SHAVER, J. R., "Studies on the initiation of cleavage in the frog egg," *J. Exptl. Zool.*, **122**, 169–192 (1953).

56. SIMON, DORIS, "La migration des cellules germinales de l'embryon de Poulet vers les ébauches gonadiques: preuvres expérimentales," *Compt. rend. Soc. Biol. (France)*, Tome **CLI**, Nos. 8–9, 1576 (1957).

57. SIMPSON, GEORGE G., *The Meaning of Evolution*, New Haven: Yale University Press, 1949.

58. SINSHEIMER, R. L., "Single-stranded DNA," *Scientific American*, **207**, 109-116 (1962).

59. SMITH, S., "Induction of triploidy in the South African clawed frog, *Xenopus laevis* (Daudin)," *Nature* **181**, 290 (1958).

60. SPEMANN, HANS, *Embryonic Development and Induction*, New Haven: Yale University Press, 1938.

61. SRB, A. M. and R. D. OWEN, *General Genetics*, San Francisco: W. H. Freeman Co., 1949.

62. SZE, L. C., cited in BARTH, L. G. and L. J. BARTH, *The Energetics of Development*, New York: Columbia University Press, 1954.

63. TAYLOR, J. H., "The time and mode of duplication of chromosomes," *Amer. Naturalist*, **XCI**, 209–221 (1957).

64. TEN CATE, G., "The intrinsic development of amphibian embryos," Dissertation. North Holland Publishing Co., Amsterdam, 1953.

65. VINCENT, W. S., Lecture at the Marine Biology Laboratory, Woods Hole, Mass., 1963.

66. WADDINGTON, C. H., *Principles of Embryology*, London: Allen and Unwin; New York: Macmillan, 1956.

67. ——, *New Patterns in Genetics and Development*, New York: Columbia University Press, 1962.

68. WARD, R. T., The origin of protein and fatty yolk in *Rana pipiens*. I and II. Electron microscopical and cytochemical observations of young and mature oocytes," *J. Cell. Biol.*, **14**, 303–341 (1962).

69. WHITAKER, D. M., "Physical factors of growth," *Growth Supplement*, 75–90 (1940).

70. WITSCHI, E., *Development of Vertebrates*, Philadelphia: Saunders, 1956.

71. WRIGHT, S., "The physiology of the gene," *Physiol. Rev.*, **21**, 487–527 (1941).

72. ——, "Genes as physiological agents," *Amer. Nat.*, **79**, 289–303 (1945).

73. YAMADA, TUNEO, "Embryonic induction," in *The Chemical Basis of Development*, W. McElroy and B. Glass, eds., Baltimore: Johns Hopkins Press, 1958.

74. ——, "The inductive phenomenon as a tool for understanding the basic mechanism of differentiation," *J. Cell. and Comp. Physiol.*, suppl. 1, **60**, 49–64 (1962).

Index

Index

---

* Page numbers in italic type indicate illustrations.